Exercises in Coastal Navigation

G W White

Stanford Maritime Limited
Member Company of the George Philip Group
27A Floral Street, London WC2E 9DP

First published in Great Britain 1965
Reprinted 1968, 1970, 1972, 1974, 1977, 1980, 1982, 1986, 1987
Copyright © 1965 G. W. White

ISBN 0 540 07265 6

CONTENTS

STANFORD MARITIME LONDON

Foreword

The following series of examples and exercises is based on my course of lectures to students of Coastal Navigation at the Ilford Literary Institute.

The main purpose of this book is to give the reader the opportunity to do a number of exercises in Coastal Navigation thus filling the gap left by many books on this subject. Although written primarily for the beginner it is hoped that the more experienced navigator may find it a useful addition to his bookshelves.

This book will also be of assistance to those already teaching Coastal Navigation or studying for G.C.E. and D.O.T./R.Y.A. Certificates.

Each exercise is, where it is thought necessary, preceded by a worked example for which purpose Admiralty Chart No. 1431 is used. The examples should be worked by the reader in addition to the exercises and since they are progressive they should be worked in numerical order.

The exercises have been worked using the following Admiralty Charts, reproductions of which are included with the book:—

(1) No. 1431 — Approaches to Dover Strait.
(2) No. 2159 — Firth of Clyde and Approaches.
(3) No. 1411 — Braich-y-Pwll to Clogher Head.

My thanks are due to the Controller of Her Majesty's Stationery Office and the Hydrographer of the Navy for permission to print the above charts. These charts should not be used for practical navigation.

The reader should provide the following drawing instruments which are necessary for coastal navigation.

1. Parallel rules or the equivalent means of transferring position lines etc., (preference for at least 15" boxwood or perspex rules).
2. Dividers (6")
3. Pencil compasses.
4. Protractor.
5. Soft pencil (not harder than 'B') and an eraser.

All positions and distances have been measured to the nearest tenth of a minute of arc, all courses to the nearest half of a degree.

I wish to thank all those who have assisted in this publication, especially those who have checked the answers, and I would be glad to hear of any large discrepancies.

HOOK END, ESSEX   G.W. WHITE

1
The Position, Course and Distance

THE POSITION

A position on a chart may be stated in one of two ways,

      (a) by the latitude and longitude,
      (b) with reference to another position by giving the bearing and distance of, or from, that position.

EXAMPLE 1

To find the latitude and longitude of South Foreland lighthouse.

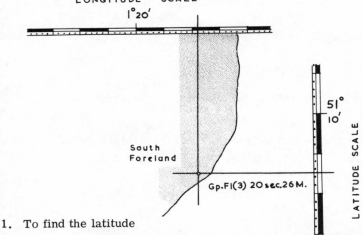

1.   To find the latitude

      Place the parallel rules on the chart with one edge set along a parallel of latitude. Carefully open them out until one edge passes through the required position. Where this edge (or the continuation of this edge) cuts the scale of latitude at the side of the chart read off the latitude of the lighthouse, i.e. $51^{\circ}08.'5N$.

2.   To find the longitude

      Place the parallel rules on the chart with one edge set along a meridian and following a similar process to that for finding the latitude, read off the longitude of the lighthouse on the scale at the top or bottom of the chart, i.e. $01^{\circ}22.'2E$.

Note:- A position is always given by the latitude and then the longitude.

      South Foreland lighthouse:- Lat. $51^{\circ}08.'5$ N. Long. $01^{\circ}22.'2$ E.

Dividers may be used to find the latitude and longitude by measuring the perpendicular distance between the nearest parallel of latitude or meridian and the required position and transferring this measurement to the appropriate scale.

EXERCISE 1

Find the latitude and longitude of the following Charted Positions.

(a) Chart No. 1431

    Dungeness Lt. Hse.
    Royal Sovereign Lt. Vessel.
    Folkestone Lt. Hse.
    C. d' Alprech Lt. Hse.
    Cap Gris Nez Lt. Hse.
    Calais High Lt. Hse. (19m)

(b) Chart No. 2159

    Pladda Lt. Hse.
    Ailsa Craig Lt. Hse.
    Corsewall Pt. Lt. Hse.
    Sanda Isle Lt. Hse.
    Davarr Isle Lt. Hse.

(c) Chart No. 1411

    Wicklow Head Lt. Hse.
    Rockabill Lt. Hse.
    Kish Lt. Vessel.
    Lynas Pt. Lt. Hse.
    Bardsey Isle Lt. Hse.

THE TRUE COURSE AND DISTANCE

EXAMPLE 2

Find the true course and distance between the following positions.

    (1) Lat. $50^\circ 30'$N. Long. $00^\circ 20'$E.
    (2) Lat. $50^\circ 40'$N. Long. $00^\circ 45'$E.

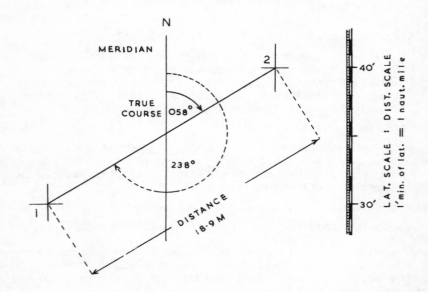

1.   Plot the two positions on the chart using the reverse procedure to that required in the previous example.

2.   Join the two positions by a straight line; this line represents the course line.

3. a.   The angle that the course line makes with the meridian, usually measured in a clockwise direction from north and given in the three figure notation, is the true course, i.e. 058°. If the true course had been required from position 2 to position 1 it would have been 238°.

   b.   To find the true course

       Set the edge of the parallel rules along the course line and carefully transfer them to the nearest compass rose, placing one edge through the exact centre of the rose. Read off the true direction from the rose taking care not to read off the reciprocal course.

4.   Using dividers and the scale of latitude between these two positions measure the distance. One nautical mile is equal to one minute of arc on the latitude scale.

       The distance between any two positions must be measured in the region of the mean latitude between them. When large distances are involved set the dividers to a convenient distance, e.g. 10 miles; step off along the course line making a note of the number of steps taken, measuring the final portion of a step separately. The distance is 18.9 miles.

       True course and distance:-   058°, 18.9 m.

EXERCISE 2

Plot the following positions on the chart and find the course and distance between the successive positions.

(a) Chart No. 1431

51° 06.'8 N., 01° 20.'0 E.
50° 53.'0 N., 01° 34.'0 E.
50° 45.'4 N., 01° 30.'0 E.
50° 30.'0 N., 01° 15.'0 E.
50° 18.'5 N., 01° 15.'0 E.
50° 24.'0 N., 00° 24.'5 E.
50° 54.'5 N., 01° 00.'0 E.
51° 06.'8 N., 01° 20.'0 E.

(b) Chart No. 2159

55° 43.'0 N., 04° 59.'0 W.
55° 31.'5 N., 04° 45.'0 W.
55° 15.'0 N., 05° 05.'0 W.
55° 00.'5 N., 05° 12.'0 W.
55° 16.'0 N., 05° 33.'5 W.
55° 25.'5 N., 05° 03.'5 W.
55° 43.'0 N., 04° 59.'0 W.

(c) Chart No. 1411

53° 36' N., 05° 58' W.
53° 19' N., 05° 52' W.
53° 04' N., 05° 40' W.
52° 45' N., 04° 50' W.
53° 18' N., 04° 45' W.
53° 40' N., 05° 15' W.
53° 36' N., 05° 58' W.

EXAMPLE 3

Given a departure position of Lat. 51° 00' N., Long. 01° 46' E. and the following successive courses and distances sailed, find the arrival position.

(a) 276°, 15 miles
(b) 242°, 17 miles

1. Plot the departure position on the chart.

2. Lay off the first course through this position and measure the distance along this line; mark this point accordingly.

3. Lay off the second course through this new position; measure the distance and find the position arrived at, namely:

Lat. 50° 53.'5 N., Long. 00° 58.'6 E.

EXERCISE 3

Given the departure position, plot the following true courses and distances consecutively and find the arrival position.

(a) Chart No. 1431   Departure position 50° 04' N., 01° 19' E.

True Course 296°	Distance 17 miles
062°	19 "
342°	34 "
242°	23 "
091°	35 "
019°	11 "

(b) Chart No. 2159   Departure position 55° 01' N., 05° 04' W.

True Course 344°	Distance 13 miles
300°	11 "
073°	24 "
326°	21 "
279°	6 "
226°	7.5 "

(c) Chart No. 1411   Departure position 52° 42' N., 04° 30' W.

True Course 296°	Distance 13 miles
036°	20 "
326°	15 "
018°	11 "
087°	12 "
111°	16 "

THE MAGNETIC AND COMPASS COURSE

The following two Deviation Tables will be used in the following examples and exercises, the appropriate table being indicated as required.

It may be argued that deviations of the magnitude shown in the tables seldom exist on board; the essential point of the exercise is for the navigator to be fully aware of the deviation that exists and the correct application of this error.

Deviation Card No. 1

Boat's Head	Dev.	Boat's Head	Dev.
North	4°W	South	6°E
N x E	6°W	S x W	9°E
N.N.E.	8°W	S.S.W.	12°E
N E x N	10°W	S W x S	13°E
N. E.	12°W	S. W.	14°E
N E x E	14°W	S W x W	14°E
E.N.E.	15°W	W.S.W.	13°E
E x N	16°W	W x S	12°E
East	15°W	West	10°E
E x S	13°W	W x N	9°E
E.S.E.	11°W	W.N.W.	7°E
S E x E	8°W	N W x W	3°E
S. E.	5°W	N. W.	1°E
S E x S	3°W	N W x N	1°W
S.S.E.	0°	N.N.W.	3°W
S x E	3°E	N x W	4°W
South	6°E	North	4°W

Deviation Card No. 2

Boat's Head	Dev.	Boat's Head	Dev.
North	16°E	South	14°W
N x E	13°E	S x W	10°W
N.N.E.	9°E	S.S.W.	7°W
N E x N	4°E	S W x S	3°W
N. E.	0°	S. W.	0°
N E x E	4°W	S W x W	3°E
E.N.E.	7°W	W.S.W.	7°E
E x N	11°W	W x S	10°E
East	14°W	West	13°E
E x S	18°W	W x N	17°E
E.S.E.	21°W	W.N.W.	20°E
S E x E	23°W	N W x W	22°E
S. E.	24°W	N. W.	23°E
S E x S	23°W	N W x N	22°E
S.S.E.	21°W	N.N.W.	21°E
S x E	18°W	N x W	19°E
South	14°W	North	16°E

In the following exercises it is to be assumed that all compass bearings are taken from the steering compass. The variation and deviation, namely the compass error, must therefore be applied to both compass bearings and compass courses.

Since the deviations have been tabulated with the boat's head given in points of the compass it is suggested that the tables should be re-tabulated to give the deviation with respect to both compass and magnetic headings using the three figure notation.

Retabulate the deviations in the following manner.

DEV. CARD No. 1			DEV. CARD No. 2		
Boat's head Compass	Dev.	Boat's head Magnetic	Boat's head Compass	Dev.	Boat's head Magnetic
000°	4^OW	356°	000°	16^OE	016°
$011\frac{1}{4}^O$	6^OW	$005\frac{1}{4}^O$	$011\frac{1}{4}^O$	13^OE	$024\frac{1}{4}^O$
$022\frac{1}{2}^O$	8^OW	$014\frac{1}{2}^O$	$022\frac{1}{2}^O$	9^OE	$031\frac{1}{2}^O$
$033\frac{3}{4}^O$	10^OW	$023\frac{3}{4}^O$	$033\frac{3}{4}^O$	4^OE	$037\frac{3}{4}^O$
045°	12^OW	033°	045°	0°	045°
etc.	etc.	etc.	etc.	etc.	etc.

When finding the deviation for any intermediate heading it is assumed that the deviation varies linearly between the various compass or magnetic headings.

This table will be of great assistance when working the examples and exercises. The two deviation cards are given in their retabulated form at the back of the book.

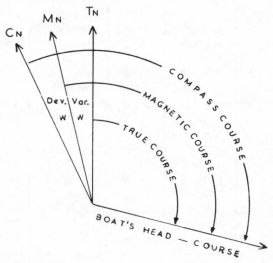

N.B. The notation (M) or (C) after the number of degrees indicates Magnetic or Compass courses or bearings respectively. No notation indicates True courses or bearings.

> i.e.   True course = 059°
> Magnetic course = 123° (M)
> Compass course = 246° (C)

EXAMPLE 4

Using Deviation Table No. 1, Variation 10° W., find the Compass Course to steer, the True Course being 072°.

1.   Apply the Variation to the True Course to obtain the Magnetic Course. True to Magnetic; Westerly Variation plus, Easterly Variation minus to the true headings or bearings.

> True course 072°
> Variation 10° W
> Magnetic course 082° (M)

2.   It is now necessary to find the Deviation corresponding to a magnetic heading of 082° (M).

Referring to Deviation Table No. 1.

Boat's head Compass	Dev.	Boat's head Magnetic
090°	15° W	075°
$101\frac{1}{4}^O$	13° W	$088\frac{1}{4}^O$

Interpolating for a magnetic heading of 082° (M) the deviation is 14° W.

N.B. The deviation changes 2^O for a change of magnetic heading of $13\frac{1}{4}^O$. Since 082° (M) is $6\frac{1}{4}^O$ from $088\frac{1}{4}^O$ (M) the correction is

$$\frac{2 \times 6\frac{1}{4}}{13\frac{1}{4}} = 1^O W \text{ (approx.)}$$

Required deviation 13° W + 1^O W = 14° W.

Apply the deviation to the magnetic course to obtain the compass course.

Magnetic to Compass; Westerly Deviation plus, Easterly Deviation minus to the magnetic headings or bearings.

> Magnetic course 082° (M)
> Deviation 14° W
> Compass course 096° (C)

The sum of the Variation and Deviation is called the Compass Error, in this instance:-

$$10^O W + 14^O W = 24^O W.$$

EXAMPLE 5

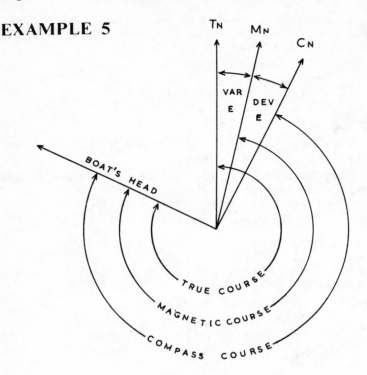

Using Deviation Table No. 2, Variation 7°E., find the true course steered, the compass course being 274°(C).

The procedure is the reverse of that used in the previous example.

1.   To find the deviation for a heading of 274°(C).

From Deviation Table No. 2

Boat's head by Compass	Deviation
270°	13° E
281¼°	17° E

Interpolating for a compass heading of 274°(C) the deviation is $14\frac{1}{2}$°E.

N.B. The deviation changes 4° for a change of compass heading of $11\frac{1}{4}$°. Since 274°(C) is 4° from 270°(C) the correction is:

$$\frac{4 \times 4}{11\frac{1}{4}} = 1\frac{1}{2}° \text{ (approx.)}$$

Required deviation $13°E + 1\frac{1}{2}°E = 14\frac{1}{2}°E$

Compass heading	274° (C)
Deviation	$14\frac{1}{2}^O$ E
Magnetic heading	$288\frac{1}{2}^O$(M)

Compass to Magnetic; Westerly deviation minus, Easterly deviation plus to the compass headings or bearings.

2.   To find the true course steered.

Magnetic heading	$288\frac{1}{2}^O$(M)
Variation	7° E
True course	$295\frac{1}{2}^O$

Magnetic to True; Westerly variation minus, Easterly variation plus to the Magnetic headings or bearings.

EXERCISE 4

(a)   Using the Deviation Table No. 1, Variation 11° W.

(i) Find the Compass Courses to steer from the following True Courses.

022°, 146°, 215°, 307°, 064°, 189°, 294°.

(ii) Find the Compass Courses to steer from the following Magnetic Courses.

045^O(M), 168^O(M), 285^O(M), 354^O(M).

(iii) Find the True Courses steered from the following Compass Courses.

037^O(C), 127^O(C), 207^O(C), 264^O(C), 319^O(C), 358^O(C).

(b).   Using the Deviation Table No. 2, Variation 16° E.

(i) Find the True Courses steered from the following Compass Courses.

042^O(C), 098^O(C), 162^O(C), 354^O(C), S 18° W, W x N $\frac{1}{4}$ N,

E x S $\frac{3}{4}$ S,   N 52° W.

(ii) Find the Compass Courses to steer from the following True Courses.

086°, 137°, 180°, 259°, 302°, 334°.

A position may be indicated by a bearing and distance from another fixed position.

EXAMPLE 6

A conical buoy is moored in a position 300° distant 8.7 miles from Cap Gris Nez lighthouse. Give the position of the buoy as latitude and longitude.

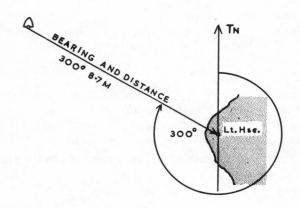

1. (a) To lay off a true bearing.

    Place the parallel rules on a compass rose such that one edge passes through the exact centre of the rose and the required true bearing. Transfer the parallel rules until one edge passes through the required position and then draw a line through this position. This is then the required bearing.

   (b) Lay off the given bearing through Cap Gris Nez lighthouse.

2.   Measure the given distance along this line of bearing from the point of reference. This will give the required position.

     Position of buoy:-   Lat. 50° 56.'6 N., Long. 01° 23.'3 E.

EXERCISE 5

Chart No. 1431

Find the compass course to steer and the distance between the following positions. Variation 9°W, Deviation Card No. 2.

(a) W. Dyck light vessel bearing   180° distant 0. 5 m.
(b) N. E. Varne light buoy bearing   180° distant 0. 5 m.
(c) Varne light vessel bearing   110° distant 1. 0 m.
(d) Royal Sovereign light vessel bearing   000° distant 1. 0 m.

Chart No. 1411

Find the compass course to steer and the distance between the following positions. Variation 10°W, Deviation Card No. 1.

(a) Wicklow Head bearing 293° distant 4 miles.
(b) 2 miles, 315° from the Codling light vessel.
(c) Kish light vessel bearing 270°, distant 3 miles.
(d) 1 mile, 107° from Bailey Lt. Hse. (Dublin Bay).

Chart No. 2159

Find the compass course to steer and the distance between the following positions. Variation 11°W, Deviation Card No. 2.

(a) Ardrossan Occ. Lt. bearing 063° distant 14 cables.
(b) Turnberry Pt. Lt. bearing   110° distant 15 cables.
(c) Corsewall Pt. Lt. bearing   180° distant 6 cables.

Give the position of Milleur Point light and bell buoy as a true bearing and distance from Corsewall Point Lt. Hse.

2
Fixing the Position

FIXING THE POSITION OF THE BOAT

In order to maintain the course laid down on the chart it is necessary to ascertain frequently the position of the boat by observations of terrestrial objects.

A position line:- any line drawn on a chart on which the position of the boat is known to be.

A fix:- the intersection of two or more position lines which have been obtained at approximately the same time will give the position of the boat.

METHODS OF OBTAINING A POSITION LINE

1. A visual bearing of a terrestrial object.
2. A radio bearing of a radio beacon.
3. A transit bearing.
4. A circle of position obtained from a vertical (sextant) angle.
5. A circle of position obtained from a horizontal (sextant) angle, or the angle between two compass bearings whether the compass error is known or not.
6. A circle of position obtained from the range of a light when seen to dip below, or rise above, the horizon.
7. A sounding or line of soundings.

EXAMPLES OF FIXING THE POSITION

EXAMPLE 7

Cross Bearings

At the same time as Cap Gris Nez bore 050°, C.d'Alprech bore 156°. Find the boat's position.

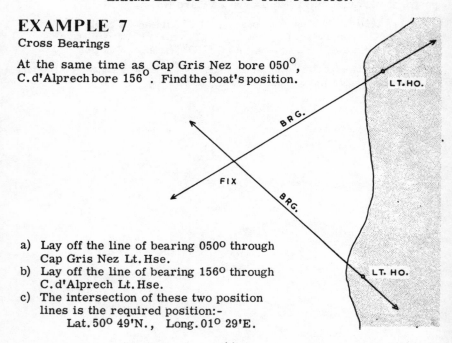

a) Lay off the line of bearing 050° through Cap Gris Nez Lt.Hse.
b) Lay off the line of bearing 156° through C.d'Alprech Lt.Hse.
c) The intersection of these two position lines is the required position:-
   Lat.50° 49'N., Long.01° 29'E.

14

EXAMPLE 8

A Transit and a Compass Bearing

Swallow Bank buoy in transit with Dungeness Lt. Hse. bore 225°(C); the tower in position Lat. 50° 59.'2 N., Long. 00° 58' E., bore 289°(C). Find the boat's position and the compass error.

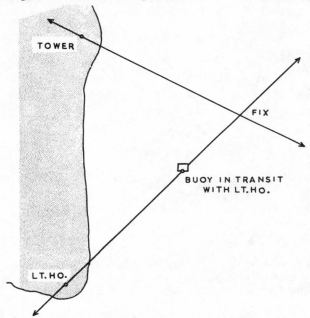

a) Since the buoy and lighthouse are in transit draw a line through these two positions. This is a transit bearing.

b) To find the compass error.

    The true bearing of the transit bearing is 218°. The difference between the true bearing and the compass bearing is the error.

True bearing	218°
Compass bearing	225°(C)
Error	7° W

c) Apply the compass error to the compass bearing of the tower to obtain the true bearing.

Compass bearing	289°(C)
Error	7° W
True bearing	282°

Lay off the true bearing through the position of the tower.

d) The intersection of the transit bearing and the true bearing of the tower is the boat's position:

Lat. 50° 58.'6 N., Long. 01° 03.'4 E.

EXAMPLE 9

Radio Bearings

At the same time as Cap Gris Nez Ro. Bn. bore 54° on the starboard bow, Dungeness Ro. Bn bore 58° on the port bow. If the boat was heading 029°(C), error 8°W., find the position.

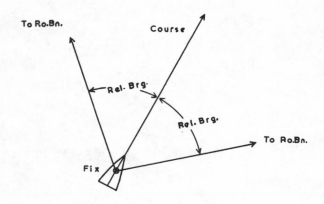

The radio bearings are given as relative bearings, bearings relative to a certain direction which in this case is the heading or course of the boat. They must be converted to true bearings before being laid off on the chart.

a) Correct the compass course to obtain the true course.

Compass course	029°(C)
Error	8°W
True course	021°

b) Apply the relative bearings to the true course to obtain the true bearings of the radio beacons.

(i) Cap Gris Nez Ro. Bn.

True course	021°
Relative brg.	54° Stbd.
True brg.	075°

(ii) Dungeness Ro. Bn.

True course	021°
Relative brg.	58° Port
True brg.	323°

c) Lay these true bearings off through their respective positions, the intersection of the two bearings fixing the boat's position:

Lat. 50° 47.'5 N., Long. 01° 07.'4 E.

EXAMPLE 10

Horizontal Angles

When the horizontal angle subtended between two terrestrial objects is known a circle of position can be drawn on the chart. The intersection of a circle of position with another position line, in this case a second position circle, will fix the position of the boat.

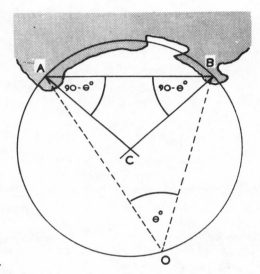

Construction:-

In the figure, A and B represent two lighthouses between which the horizontal angle θ^o has been measured.

   i. Join A and B by a straight line.

  ii. At A and B lay off on the same side as the observer the complement of the horizontal angle, namely 90° — horizontal angle $(90^o - \theta^o)$.

 iii. The point of intersection of these two lines, at C, is the centre of the circle which passes through A, B and the observer.

Note:- When the horizontal angle is greater than 90° the centre of the position circle lies on the opposite side of the line joining the two objects to that of the observer. Subtract 90° from the observed angle and proceed as above.

The following compass bearings were obtained from a boat:

Treport Gp. Fl. (2) Lt.	bore	173° (C)
Ault Lt.	bore	138° (C)
Cayeux Fl. R. 18 m. Lt.	bore	087° (C)

If the boat was heading 030^o(C), Variation 16^oW., find the position of the boat and the deviation for this compass heading.

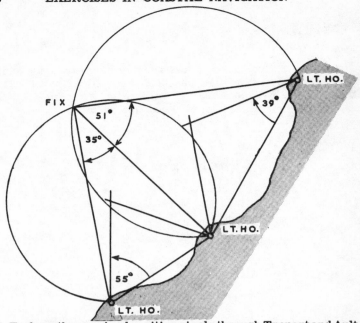

a) To draw the required position circle through Treport and Ault Lt.

   i.   Join the two objects between which the angle has been measured by a straight line.

  ii.   Since the compass bearing of Treport Lt. is 173^O(C) and Ault Lt. 138^O(C) the horizontal angle subtended is 35°.

 iii.   At each lighthouse lay off, on the same side as the observer, the complement of the horizontal angle, i.e. 90° - 35° = 55°.

 iv.   The point of intersection of these two lines is the centre of the required circle which passes through the two objects (lighthouses) observed and the observer.

  v.   Draw in the required circle of position.

b) Using a similar construction to the above draw the circle of position through Ault Lt., Cayeux Lt. and the observer. The horizontal angle is 51°.

c) The intersection of these two position circles gives the position of the observer:- Lat. 50° 10.'5 N., Long. 01° 19.'8 E.

d) To find the deviation

The position of the boat having been ascertained the true bearings of the lights can be taken from the chart. The difference between the true and compass bearing will give the error.

Ault Lt.	true bearing	130°
	comp. bearing	138° (C)
	error	8° W
	variation	16° W
	deviation	8° E

EXAMPLE 11
The Maximum Range of a Light and a Bearing

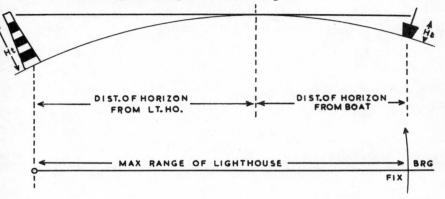

The distance of the horizon will depend on the height of the observer's eye, object etc. It may be calculated as follows:-

$$\text{distance (d) of horizon} = 1.15\sqrt{h}$$

where d = distance in miles
h = height of eye in feet

(i)   A shore light, ht. 100 ft., is observed to dip, height of eye 9 ft. Calculate the distance of the light from the observer.

Dist. of horizon from the light	$= 1.15\sqrt{100} = 11.5\text{m}$
Dist. of horizon from the observer	$= 1.15\sqrt{9}\ \ = 3.45\text{m}$
Dist. of light from observer	$= \overline{14.95\text{m}}$
	or approx. 15 miles

The distance of the sea horizon for various heights of eye is tabulated in Reeds Nautical Almanac and other publications.

(ii)   Approaching Somme Bay from the west, heading 119°(C), Cayeux Fl. R. Lt. 18m., was observed to rise bearing 126°(C). If the height of eye is 15 ft., compass error 29°W, find the position.

The range of visibility of lights shown on the chart is calculated for a height of the observer's eye of 15 ft. In this case the charted range being 18 miles the light will just appear above, or dip below, the horizon at this range.

a) Lay off the true bearing of the light.

Compass bearing	126° (C)
Error	29° W
True bearing	097°

b) Measure off the distance of the observer from the light, i.e. 18 miles. This is the required position:-

Lat. 50° 14' N., Long. 01° 03'.3 E.

EXAMPLE 12

A Vertical Sextant Angle and a Bearing

A boat off Beachy Head observed the lighthouse, height 103 ft.,to subtend a vertical sextant angle of $0^o 45'$, bearing 022°.   Find the position.

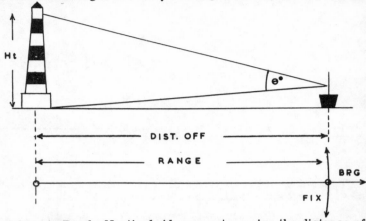

Tables in Reeds Nautical Almanac etc., give the distance off the lighthouse, in this instance 1.3 miles.

a) Lay off the true bearing of the lighthouse.

b) Measure the required distance from the light, 1.3 miles, this will give the position:-

Lat. $50^o 42'.8$ N., Long. $00^o 14'$ E.

EXAMPLE 13

A Sounding and a Bearing

The Royal Sovereign light vessel was observed bearing 326° at the same time as a sounding gave 20 fathoms.   Find the position.

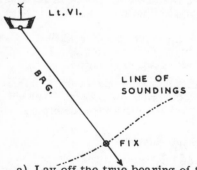

An approximate position line can be obtained from soundings. In this case the boat is in 20 fathoms.

a) Lay off the true bearing of the lighthouse, 326°.

b) Where this line of bearing crosses the 20 fathom line is the approximate position:-

Lat. $50^o 39'.8$ N., Long. $00^o 30'.0$ E.

Note:- In coastal waters where the rise of the tide is appreciable the height of the tide above chart datum must be subtracted from the sounding obtained before consulting the chart.

EXERCISE 6

Chart No. 1431

Find the position of the boat in each of the following exercises. Variation 7°W., Deviation Card No. 1. throughout.

(a) Cross Bearings

On a course of 191°(C), Paris Plage Lt. bore 052°(C) and at the same time Pte. du Haut Banc Lt. bore 143°(C).

(b) Transit and Bearing

Heading 275°(C), the NE Varne lightbuoy was seen to be in transit with the Varne light vessel and at the same time South Foreland Lt. Hse. bore 331°(C).

(c) Horizontal Angles

The following horizontal angles were observed from a boat:-

Folkestone Lt.   100° Varne light vessel 130° Dungeness Lt.

N. B. Written as such this means that the angle subtended by Folkestone light and the Varne lightvessel was 100°, and between the Varne light vessel and Dungeness light was 130°.

(d) Maximum Range and Bearing

Heading 079° (C) the Varne Lt. V. was observed to rise bearing 092°(C) at the charted range.

(e) Radio Bearing and Sounding

Heading 199° (C) in foggy weather off the French Coast, a D. F. bearing of Cap Gris Nez was obtained bearing 20° abaft the port beam. At the same time a sounding gave 20 fathoms.

(f) Vertical Sextant Angle and Bearing

Heading 063°(C) a vertical sextant angle of Cap Gris Nez Lt. Hse. measured 1° 01' when the lighthouse was abeam.

EXERCISE 7

Chart No. 2159

Find the position of the boat in the following exercises.

(a) Cross Bearings

   Heading 203^O(C), Turnberry Pt. Lt. was observed bearing 065^O(C) and Girvan Occ. Lt. to bear 166^O(C). Deviation Card No.1., Variation 10^OW.

(b) Transit and Bearing

   Heading 317^O(C), Garrock Head was observed in transit with Lit. Cumbrae Lt. Hse. bearing 099^O(C). At the same time the western edge of Inch Marnoch bore 344^O(C). If the variation is 11^OW., find the position and the deviation for this compass heading.

(c) Radio and Visual Bearing

   Heading 352^O(C), the radio beacon on Lit. Cumbrae was heard 10° on the starboard bow; at the same time the Alt. Fl.W.R. light on Holy Island bore 252^O(C). Deviation Card No. 2, Variation 10^OW.

(d) Horizontal Angles

   Heading 170^O(C), the following simultaneous compass bearings were obtained.

   i.   Lit. Cumbrae Lt. bore 352^O(C).
   ii. Ardrossan Occ. Lt. bore 049^O(C).
   iii. Lady Is. Lt. bore 112^O(C).

   If the Variation is 10^OW., find the position and deviation for this compass heading.

(e) Range and Bearing

   Approaching Pladda Isle, heading 052^O(C) the light was observed to rise bearing 042^O(C) at its charted range. Variation 10^OW. Deviation Card No.1.

(f) Transit and Horizontal Angle

   Off Lady Is. Lt., the light was observed to be in transit with Monkton Hill Air Alt. Lt. and at the same time the horizontal angle between Lady Is. Lt. and Lit. Cumbrae Lt. was 120°.

(g) Vertical Angle and Bearing

Sailing to the west of Ailsa Craig the top of the island subtended a vertical angle of $3^O 12'$ on a compass bearing of 114^O(C). Compass heading 225^O(C), Deviation Card No. 2, Variation for the year 1965.

(h) Bearing and Sounding

Heading 290^O(C), Pladda Is. Lt. bore 009^O(C) and at the same time a sounding gave 27 fathoms, the arming on the hand lead showing mud and sand. Deviation Card No. 2, Variation 10^OW. Find the approximate position.

EXERCISE 8

Chart No. 1411

Find the position of the boat in each of the following exercises. Variation 9^OW., Deviation Card No. 2 throughout.

(a) Cross Bearings

Heading 258^O(C) the Skerries Lt. Hse. was observed bearing 243^O(C) and at the same time Lynas Pt. Lt. Hse. bore 137^O(C).

(b) Transit and Bearing

Heading 188^O(C) Arklow Bank No. 1 whistle buoy was observed in transit with Wicklow Head Lt. Hse. at the same time as Arklow Bank No. 2 R. buoy bore 255^O(C).

(c) Maximum Range and Bearing

Steering 016^O(C) Wicklow Head Lt. was observed to rise bearing 293^O(C)., height of observer's eye 9 feet.

(d) Horizontal Angles

The following horizontal sextant angles were obtained; Skerries Lt. Hse. 46° Lynas Pt. Lt. Hse. 74° Great Ormes Head Lt. Hse.

(e) Bearing and Sounding

Whilst rounding the Skerries on a course of 256^O(C) a bearing of the Skerries Lt. Hse. was 177^O(C) and at the same time the lead-line showed a corrected depth of 20 fathoms.

(f) Vertical and Horizontal Angles

Off Holyhead Bay the horizontal angle subtended by the Skerries Lt. Hse. and S. Stack Lt. Hse. was 62° and at the same time the vertical angle subtended by the S. Stack Lt. Hse. was $0^O 37'$.

THE DEAD RECKONED, D.R. POSITION

This is the position of the boat found from the courses steered and speed through the water. It is only an approximate position.

THE ESTIMATED POSITION, E. POSITION

The position of the boat when all factors, namely wind and tidal streams, have been taken into account. It is the closest estimate to the actual position that can be made.

TO FIND THE COURSE TO STEER TO COUNTERACT A CURRENT

EXAMPLE 14

Find the course to steer to counteract a tidal stream setting 026° at 2.0 knots, to make good a course of 315°, speed of boat 7 knots.

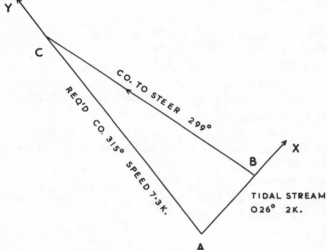

1.   Lay off the course it is required to make good, AY, 315°.
2.   From A lay off the direction, AX, of the tidal stream, 026°. Mark off the distance of the tidal stream for a convenient period of time, namely 1 hour, AB, 2 miles.
3.   From B, using compasses or dividers, and radius equal to the distance the boat can sail in the same period of time, draw an arc BC, 7 miles, to cut AY at C. The direction of BC is the required course to steer i.e. 299°.
4.   The length of AC will represent the distance made good by the boat along the line AY in the same period of time, i.e. 7.35 miles in 1 hour.

TO FIND THE COURSE AND DISTANCE (SPEED) MADE GOOD

EXAMPLE 15

A boat heading 130ᵁ at 5 knots experiences a tidal stream setting 240°
at 1½ knots. Find the course and speed made good.

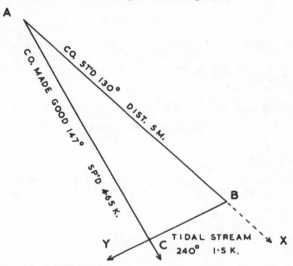

1.   Lay off from an initial position, A, the direction in which the boat
is heading, AX, 130°.

2.   Mark off on this line from A the distance the boat will sail in a
convenient period of time i.e. 5 miles in 1 hour, AB.

3.   From B lay off the direction of the tidal stream, BY, 240°.

4.   Mark off on this line from B a distance equal to the set of the tidal
stream in the above period of time i.e. 1.5 miles in 1 hour, BC.

5.   Join A to C. The direction of this line gives the course made good,
the distance AC being the distance made good in the allotted period
of time, i.e. 4.65 m. in 1 hour. Speed made good is 4.65 knots,
the course made good 147°.

Note:- When the tide is ahead or astern the course made good is the
same as that steered. The speed made good is equal to the boat's speed
minus or plus the rate of the tide.

EXERCISE 9

1.   Find the true course and speed made good. Boat steering 280°
at 7 knots, tide setting 203° at 1 knot.

2.   Tide setting 027° at 1½ knots, boat's speed 6½ knots. Find the
true course to steer to make good a course of 293°.

3.   Steering 063° at 7 knots, tide setting 099° at 1 knot, find the true
course and speed made good.

4.   It is required to make good a course of 027°, current setting 341°
at ¾ knot, boat's speed 6 knots. Find the true course and speed
made good.

3
Effect of
Current and Wind

LEEWAY

Under adverse weather conditions a boat will make a certain amount of leeway. The amount to be allowed depends on the type of the boat, strength and direction of wind etc.

There are two conditions to be considered:

(a) To find the course to steer making an allowance for leeway.

(b) To find the course made good allowing for leeway.

EXAMPLE 16

(a) It is required to make good a course of 193°, allowing 8° leeway for a SE'ly wind. If the compass error is 4°E find the compass course to steer.

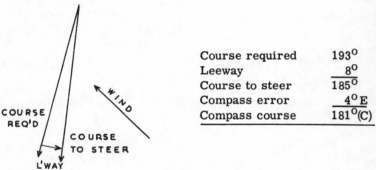

Course required	193°
Leeway	8°
Course to steer	185°
Compass error	4°E
Compass course	181^{O}(C)

In this case since it is required to make good a course of 193° the allowance for leeway is to windward.

(b) A boat heading 326^{O}(C), error 5°W., observes she is making 10° leeway. Wind NE'ly, force 5. Find the course made good.

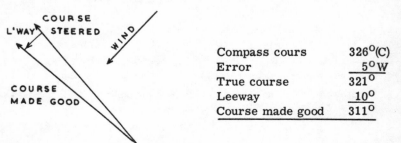

Compass cours	326^{O}(C)
Error	5°W
True course	321°
Leeway	10°
Course made good	311°

In this case since the boat is heading 326^{O}(C) the allowance for leeway is to leeward.

EXAMPLE 17

Find the course to steer to make good a course of 080° allowing for a tidal stream setting 108° at 2 knots. Boat's speed 6.5 knots, leeway 10° for a SSE wind.

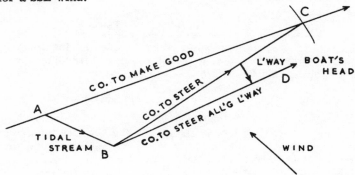

1. Find the course to steer as in a previous example allowing for the tidal stream i.e. 072°, (BC).

2. Since the wind is from the SSE, leeway 10°, the boat must head a further 10° into the wind.

Course to steer, no leeway (BC)	072°
Leeway	10°
Course to steer, allowing leeway(BD)	082°

EXAMPLE 18

A boat heading 135°(C)., error 8°W., leeway 12° for an ENE wind, experiences a current of 263° at 1.5 knots. If the speed of the boat is 5.5 knots, find the course and speed made good through the water.

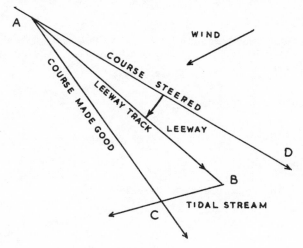

1.   To find the boat's track through the water allowing for leeway.

Compass course	135^O(C)
Error	8° W
True course (AD)	127°
Leeway, wind E N E	12°
Boat's track, leeway course (AB)	139°

2.   To find the course and speed made good allowing for the tidal stream: proceed as in a previous example measuring the speed of the boat along the boat's track or leeway course, (AB).

Course and speed made good (AC), 154°, 4.8 knots.

EXERCISE 10

1.   Heading 307^O(C)., allowing 10° leeway for a strong Westerly wind and with the tidal stream setting 264° at $1\frac{3}{4}$ knots, find the true course and speed made good. Deviation Card No. 2, Variation 6° E., speed of boat 4 knots.

2.   Find the compass course to steer and speed made good, to make good a course of 139°, tide setting 304° at 2 knots and allowing 10° leeway for a strong S'ly wind. Boat's speed 6 knots. Deviation Card No. 1, Variation 16° W.

3.   A boat is heading 040^O(C) at 6 knots, leeway 7° for a N'ly wind, tide setting 120° at 2 knots. Find the true course and speed made good. Variation 6° W., Deviation Card No. 1.

4.   Find the compass course to steer to make good a course of 219°, tidal stream 327° at 1.8 knots, allowance for leeway 10° for an ESE wind. Speed of boat 8 knots, Variation 6° E., Deviation Card No. 2.

ESTIMATED TIME OF ARRIVAL (E.T.A.)

It is frequently necessary to estimate the time of arrival at a particular point.

EXAMPLE 19

A vessel making good a speed of 6.5 knots has 24 miles to cover. How long will it take her to reach her destination and at what time if she departs at 1200 hours?

$$\text{time} = \frac{\text{distance}}{\text{speed}} = \frac{24}{6.5} = 3.692 \text{ hrs.}$$

$$= 3 \text{ hrs. } 42 \text{ mins.}$$

$$\text{E.T.A.} = 1542 \text{ hrs.}$$

EXAMPLE 20

The time interval between two bearings of a lighthouse is 48 minutes, boat's speed 7.5 knots. Calculate the distance run.

$$\text{distance} = \text{time x speed}$$

$$= \frac{48}{60} \text{ x } 7.5$$

$$= 6 \text{ miles.}$$

TO FIND THE DIRECTION AND RATE OF THE TIDAL STREAM
EXPERIENCED

1. Boat's position is at A. A course is then set from this position
    to a position G. The tidal stream being unknown, this course is
    steered.

2. A fix, after one hour, put the boat's position at C. The D.R.
    position being at B, then BC is the direction and rate of the
    tidal stream experienced.

EXAMPLE 21

From a position with C. d'Alprech Lt.Hse. bearing 090° distant 1 mile
the course was set to a position with Treport Gp.Fl(2).Lt. bearing 180°
distant 3 miles.

After sailing on this course for two hours, boat's speed 6 knots,
Paris Plage Lt. bore 057° and Pte.du Haut Banc Lt. bore 125°

(i)   Find the direction and rate of the tidal stream experienced.

(ii) Find the course to steer from the fix by cross bearings to reach
the position off Treport allowing for a similar tide to that experienced
in the first two hours.

1. To find the direction and rate of the tidal stream.

    a) Plot the departure and arrival positions and the course line on
       the chart.
    b) From the position off C. d'Alprech measure along the course
       line a distance of 12 miles, the distance covered in 2 hours.
       This position is the D.R. position.
    c) Fix the boat's position by cross bearings; this is the actual
       position of the boat.
    d) Since the boat is at the position given by the fix and not the D.R.
       position, the direction and distance of the fix from the D.R.
       position gives the direction and rate of the tidal stream, i.e.
       214° distant 3.4 m., 1.7 knots.

2. To find the course to steer

    a) Draw the new course line from the fix to the position off Treport.
    b) Find the course to steer from the fix allowing for a current
       setting 214° at 1.7 knots to make good this new course line,
       namely 179°.

TO PASS A POINT AT A GIVEN DISTANCE OFF

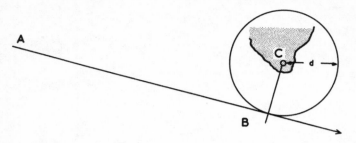

1.   With pencil compasses set to the required distance (d) draw a circle round the object.

2.   From the departure position (A) draw a line tangential to this circle (AB), this is the required course line.

3.   A line at right angles to the course line (BC) drawn through the centre of the object will give the position of the boat (B) when the object is abeam on the approach course.

EXERCISE 11

Chart No. 1431   Variation 6°W., Deviation Card No. 1.

With the boat's head on 180^{O}(C)., at 0932 hrs., South Foreland Lt. Hse. bore 283^{O}(C)., South Goodwin Lt.V. bore 045^{O}(C). The course was then set to a position with Dungeness Lt. Hse. abeam on the approach course, distant $1\frac{1}{2}$ miles.

At 1012 hrs. whilst on this course Folkestone Lt. Hse. bore 263^{O}(C) and at the same time S. Foreland Lt. Hse. bore 348^{O}(C).

Find :-

1. the compass course to steer and the distance from the position at 0932 hrs. to the position off Dungeness and the E.T.A. (estimated time of arrival), boat's speed 6 knots.

2. the direction and rate of the tidal stream experienced.

3. the compass course to steer and the new E.T.A., assuming the direction and rate of the tidal stream remains constant, from the position at 1012 hrs. to the original position off Dungeness.

EXERCISE 12

Chart No. 2159   Variation 9°W., Deviation Card No. 2.

Heading 133^{O}(C). At 1800 hrs. the Ship lighthouse bore 013^{O}(C)., at the same time as Paterson Rock bell buoy bore 063^{O}(C). Course was then set from this position to a position with Pladda lighthouse bearing 279^{O}(M) distant 1 mile, to counteract a tide setting 340° at 0.7 knots, boat's speed 7 knots.

At 2040 hrs. Pladda lighthouse bore 320^{O}(C)., and at the same time Holy Is. Alt. Fl. W. R. light bore 022^{O}(C).

Find the actual set and drift experienced between fixes.

EXERCISE 13

Chart No. 1411   Variation 8°W., Deviation Card No. 1.

From a position with Great Ormes Head Lt. Hse. bearing 108°(M)., and the centre of Puffin Island bearing 228°(M)., a course was set to a position with Lynas Pt. Lt. Hse. bearing 188°(M)., distant 1 mile to counteract a tide setting 070° estimated at $1\frac{1}{2}$ knots.

After sailing for two hours at 5 knots the following fix was obtained with Moelfre Lt. Hse. bearing 194°(C) and Lynas Pt. Lt. Hse. bearing 264°(C).

Find the actual direction and rate of the tidal stream experienced.

THE RUNNING FIX OR TRANSFERRED POSITION LINE

When two position lines are obtained at different times then the position of the boat can be fixed by transferring the first position line to intersect the second position line. The accuracy of this method depends on the course and distance made good between bearings being known.

EXAMPLE 22

At 1200 hrs. Dungeness Lt. Hse. bore 295° and at 1254 hrs. the lighthouse bore 020°. Course 237°, speed 6 knots, tidal stream 270° at 1 knot. Find the position of the boat at 1254 hrs.

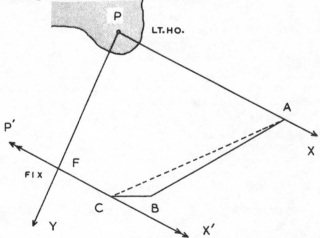

1.   Lay off the two bearings obtained, i.e. 295° and 020°. (PX and PY)
2.   From any point, A, on the first bearing lay off the course and distance sailed for the time interval between the bearings i.e. 237°, 5.4 miles (AB).
3.   From the point B lay off the effect of the tidal stream i.e. 270°, 0.9 miles (BC). AC represents the course and distance made good between bearings.
4.   Through C draw the transferred position line X'P', parallel to XP to cut the second position line at F. This is the boat's position at the time of taking the second bearing.

Lat. 50° 50.'1 N., Long. 00° 56' E.

EXERCISE 14

Chart No. 1431

1.   Approaching Boulogne on a course of 063°(C)., C. d'Alprech lighthouse bore 078°(C)., and 42 minutes later the lighthouse bore 109°(C).
The direction and rate of the tidal stream was 019° at 1 knot. Find the
position at the time of the second bearing. Variation 6°W., no deviation.
Speed of boat 6.5 knots.

2.   Heading 048°(C)., at 1415 hrs. Cap Gris Nez lighthouse bore
088°(C)., and at 1530 hrs. the lighthouse bore 173°(C). Boat's speed
6 knots, tidal stream 208° at 2 knots. Variation 6°W., Deviation Card
No. 2.   Find the position of the boat at 1530 hrs.

EXERCISE 15

Chart No. 2159

1.   Heading 028° off Ailsa Craig the lighthouse was observed bearing
328° and 40 minutes later it bore 239°. If the tide was setting 010° at
1.2 knots during this time, find the position of the boat at the time of
taking the second bearing. Speed of boat 6 knots.

2.   Sailing to the south of the Isle of Arran, Pladda light was observed bearing 300°(C) at 2337 hrs. Compass course of boat 262°(C).
At 0043 hrs. a second bearing of the light was 046°(C). During this
interval the direction and rate of the tidal stream was 136° at 0.6 knots,
speed of boat 7.5 knots. Find the position of the boat at 0043 hrs. Variation $10\frac{1}{2}$°W., Deviation Card No. 1.

EXERCISE 16

Chart No. 1411

1.   On a course of 349°(C)., boat's speed 7 knots, no tide, the Codling
lightvessel bore 308°(C)., and 1 hour later it bore 233°(C). Find the
position of the boat at the time of taking the second bearing. Variation
7°W., Deviation Card No. 1.

2.   Heading 195°(C) off Braich-y-Pwll, the tide setting 136° at 1 knot,
Bardsey Is. light was observed bearing 137°(C) and 45 minutes later the
light bore 072°(C). Find the position of the boat at the time of taking
the second bearing. Speed of boat 8 knots. Variation 7°W., Deviation
Card No. 1.

TO FIND THE COURSE MADE GOOD-THE THREE BEARING PROBLEM

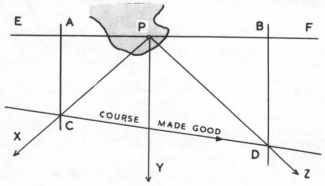

PX, PY and PZ are three bearings of the same object taken at different times.

Through P draw the line EF in any direction and set off A and B on this line such that PA and PB are proportional to the time intervals between the bearings.

Draw AC, BD parallel to the middle bearing PY.

Join C to D, this will be the course made good.

NOTE:- This line only represents the direction of the course made good and is not the actual track of the vessel.

EXAMPLE 23

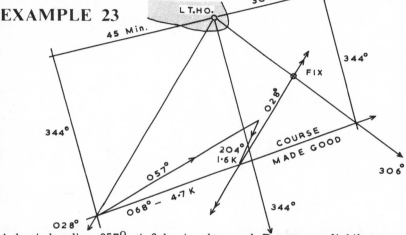

A boat heading 057° at 6 knots observed Dungeness lighthouse on a bearing of 028°.   45 minutes later the lighthouse bore 344° and after a further 30 minutes it bore 306°. If the tide was setting 204° find the course and speed made good, the rate of the tidal stream and the position of the boat at the time of taking the final bearing.

1. Lay off the three bearings through the lighthouse.
2. Draw a line in any direction through the lighthouse and set off on this line distances on either side of the lighthouse proportional to the time intervals between the bearings, i.e. 45 minutes and 30 minutes.
3. Through these points draw lines parallel to the centre bearing to cut the first and third bearings.
4. Join these two points of intersection, this will be the course made good namely 068°.
    This line only represents the direction of the course made good and is not the actual track of the vessel.
5. Since the direction of the tidal stream, the course and speed of the boat and the course made good are known the triangle of velocities can now be completed.
    Rate of tidal stream 1.6 knots, speed made good 4.7 knots.
6. The position of the boat at the time of taking the third bearing may now be found by means of a running fix.
    Position:- Lat. 50° 52.'6 N., Long. 01° 03.'6 E.

EXERCISE 17

Chart No. 1431   Variation 6°W., Deviation Card No. 1. throughout.

1.   Steering 057°(C) off Somme Bay, speed 7 knots, Pte. du Haut Banc light bore 079°(C) at 0200 hrs. One hour later it bore 088°(C) and after a further 43 minutes the light bore 108°(C)., at the same time Paris Plage light bore 060°(C).

Required the set and drift experienced since 0200 hrs. and the position at 0343 hrs.

2.   From the position at 0343 hrs. the course was set to a position 270° distant 1 mile from C. d'Alprech Lt. Hse. Find the compass course to steer to this position allowing for a similar tide to that experienced in the previous question.

3.   Off Ault light, a boat heading 214°(C)., observed the following bearings of the lighthouse:-

    a) 157°(C)., log distance 20 m.
    b) 109°(C)., log distance 24 m.
    c) 082°(C)., log distance $27\frac{1}{2}$ m.

Find the drift of the current, the direction being 278°(M).

EXERCISE 18

Chart No. 2159

1.   Heading 222°(C)., the following bearings of Ailsa Craig lighthouse were observed:-

    a) 272°(C).,   log reading 32.5
    b) 310°(C).,   log reading 35.5
    c) 353°(C).,   log reading 40.5

Find the true course made good between bearings.

Variation 10°W., Deviation Card No. 2.

2.   Heading 032°(C)., off Corsewall Pt. Lt. Hse. the following bearings of the lighthouse were observed:-

    a) ·1410 hrs., bearing 065°(C).
    b) 1455 hrs., bearing 116°(C).
    c) 1530 hrs., bearing 156°(C).

During this time the direction of the tidal stream was known to be 239°. The boat's speed was 7 knots.

Find:-   i.   the true course made good between 1410 hrs. and 1530 hrs.

        ii. the rate of the tidal stream.

       iii. the position at 1530 hrs.

Variation 10°W., Deviation Card No. 1.

Chart No. 1411

1.   A vessel heading 270°(C) at 5 knots observed Lynas Pt. lighthouse bearing 243°(C) at 1012 hrs. At 1052 hrs. the lighthouse bore 199°(C) and at 1145 hrs. it bore 127°(C)., and at the same time the Skerries lighthouse bore 247°(C). Variation 10°W., Deviation Card No. 1.

Give the position of the boat at 1012 hrs. and 1145 hrs., the direction and rate of the tidal stream experienced, the distance off and time when the boat will have the Skerries lighthouse abeam, assuming the tidal stream remains constant in direction and rate.

2.   A boat heading 185°(C) at 7 knots observed the following bearings of Rockabill lighthouse. At 0030 hrs. bearing 233°(C)., 0100 hrs. bearing 285°(C)., and at 0130 hrs. bearing 326°(C). At 0130 hrs. a bearing of Bailey Head lighthouse was 235°(C). Find the direction and rate of the tidal stream experienced and the position at 0130 hrs. Variation 10°W. Deviation Card No. 2.

Assuming the tidal stream to remain constant in direction and strength, find the compass course to steer to reach a position with the Kish lightvessel bearing 270° distant 1 mile, and the E.T.A. off the lightvessel.

CHARTED TIDAL STREAMS

The direction and rate of the tidal stream in practice is taken from the Table of Tidal Streams shown on the chart or from an Atlas of Tidal Streams covering the appropriate area.

The following example and exercises are worked using the tables printed on the chart.

The tables give the direction and rate of the tidal stream over a period of 6 hours before and after High Water at a particular Standard Port. The rates are tabulated for Spring and Neap tides and should be interpolated when the state of the tide lies between these values.

EXAMPLE 24

A yacht in position off the Royal Sovereign lightvessel, at 1400 hours, requires to know the direction and rate of the tidal stream for the next hour. High water Dover 1155 hrs., three days after spring tides.

The time difference for which the direction and rate is required is between 2 and 3 hours after high water at Dover. It is therefore necessary to take the average direction and rate between these two times. From table ◈ position 50° 42.'7 N., 00° 27' E., the following information is extracted:

	Direction	Rate	
		Springs	Neaps
2 hrs. after H.W.	247°	1.4	0.8
3 hrs. after H.W.	248°	1.8	1.0
Average values	248°	1.6	0.9

Since three days have elapsed from spring tides, there being seven days between spring and neap tides, it is necessary to interpolate between the values obtained for spring and neap tides.

The required direction and rate is 248° at 1.3 knots.

EXERCISE 20

Give the direction and rate of the tidal stream in the following cases:-

Chart No. 1431   HIGH WATER DOVER 1823 Hrs.

1. 1520 hrs., neap tides, off Dungeness.
2. 2000 hrs., spring tides, off Cap Gris Nez.
3. 2200 hrs., 3 days before spring tides, off C. d'Alprech.
4. between 1300 hrs. and 1400 hrs., 2 days after neap tides in position 50° 43' N., 01° 00' E.

Chart No. 1411   HIGH WATER LIVERPOOL 1011 Hrs.

5. 1200 hrs., spring tides, off Codling lightvessel.
6. 0840 hrs., neap tides, in Caernarvon Bay.
7. 1445 hrs., 3 days before spring tides, in Beaumaris Bay.
8. between 0640 hrs. and 0740 hrs., 2 days after spring tides, when off Kish lightvessel.

Chart No. 2159   HIGH WATER GREENOCK 0206 Hrs. and 1457 Hrs.

9. 0340 hrs., neap tides, to west of Lit. Cumbrae Is.
10. 1200 hrs., 2 days after spring tides, off Sanda Is.
11. 1820 hrs., 3 days before spring tides, in position 55°20'N.,05°00'W.
12. between 1800 hrs. and 1900 hrs., spring tides, in the Bute Sound.

EXERCISE 21

Chart No. 1431   Variation $6\frac{1}{2}°$W., Deviation Card No. 2.

1.   Find the true course and distance from a position with the Royal Sovereign lightvessel bearing 360° distant 1 mile, to the Occ. R.Whistle buoy off Boulogne.

2.   Assuming the course is adjusted every two hours, find the compass courses to steer allowing for the tidal stream as per chart. The boat is off the Royal Sovereign Lt.V. at 0930 hrs., speed 6 knots, high water Dover 1135 hrs. and 2355 hrs., spring tides.

3.   Assuming the final course is carried through to the buoy, calculate the E.T.A. off Boulogne.

4.   Find the position of the boat after 6 hours if no allowance had been made for the tidal stream.

EXERCISE 22

Chart No. 2159   Variation $10\frac{1}{2}^O$ W., Deviation Card No. 1.

1.   Find the true course and distance from a position with Lit. Cumbrae Lt. Hse. bearing 090° distant 5 cables to a position with Ailsa Craig Lt. Hse. bearing 270° distant 10 cables.

2.   A boat is at the position off Lit. Cumbrae at noon, speed 7 knots, high water Greenock 1423 hrs., spring tides.

Find the compass courses to steer, adjusting the course every hour, to reach the position off Ailsa Craig. Tidal streams as per chart. Assume ◈Ⓕ for the 1st hour, ◈Ⓔ for the 2nd hour and ◈Ⓘ for the remainder of the passage. Give the E.T.A. off Ailsa Craig.

3.   A boat off Sanda Island at 1600 hrs., H.W. 2100 hrs. at Greenock, spring tides, wishes to make good a course of 235°. Find the compass course to steer and the speed made good. Tidal stream as per chart, boat's speed 6 knots, leeway 5° for a SSE'ly wind.

EXERCISE 23

Chart No. 1411

1.   Find the true courses and distances from a position with the Kish lightvessel bearing 270° distant 1 mile to a position 270° distant 2 miles from the Codling lightvessel, thence to a position with No. 5 Arklow Bank buoy bearing 270° distant 1 mile.

2.   Taking the direction and rate of the tidal streams from the chart and with the boat off the Kish lightvessel at 0830 hrs. find the compass courses to steer to reach the position off No. 5 buoy and the E.T.A. off the Codling Lt.V. and No. 5 buoy. Speed of boat 8 knots; Variation $7\frac{1}{2}^O$ W, Deviation Card No. 1. Adjust compass courses every hour for the appropriate tidal stream:

Assume under ◈Ⓗ for the 1st hour
"   "   ◈Ⓖ "   " 2nd and 3rd hours
"   "   ◈Ⓕ "   " 4th hour
"   "   ◈Ⓔ "   " 5th hour.

High water at Liverpool, 1200 hrs., spring tides.

4
Plotting the Boat's Track

SAILING TO WINDWARD

A number of problems arise from the inability of a sailing vessel to sail directly into the wind. The yachtsman has therefore to tack or beat to windward.

The following examples show how to keep a plot of the boat's track through the water. It is essential to keep a continuous plot of the boat's track taking into account changes in the wind direction, direction and rate of the tidal stream etc.

Whenever possible a fix should be obtained adjusting the track as necessary.

In the following examples and exercises the following conditions have been made to obtain uniformity of answers:-

1. The extent of the track either side of the original course line will be given, e.g. 3 miles either side of the original course line.
2. The initial tack is that which lies closest to the original course line.
3. The last but one tack is only of sufficient length such that the final tack takes the boat directly to her destination.

Since the compass heading is dependant on the wind direction, the exercise resolves into finding the course and speed made good on each tack allowing for leeway and tidal stream.

TO FIND THE COURSE AND SPEED MADE GOOD WHEN BEATING TO WINDWARD

EXAMPLE 25

A yacht sailing close hauled into a SE wind has a speed of 5 knots. If she is able to sail within 45° of the wind, find the course and speed made good:

      a) when on the port tack
      b) when on the starboard tack.

The allowance for leeway is estimated as 10° and the tidal stream to be setting 330° at 2 knots.

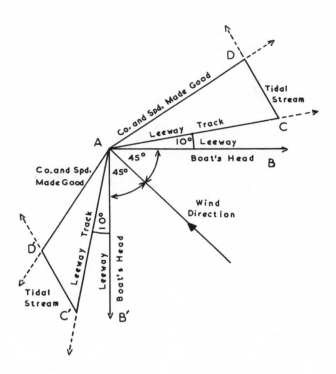

1. Plot the position of the yacht, A.
2. Draw in the direction of the wind, SE.
3. Since the vessel can only sail within a certain number of degrees of the wind, in this instance 45°, draw lines 45° either side of the wind direction to represent the direction of the boat's head. This will be 090° and 180° depending on the tack.
4. Draw lines 10° to leeward of the boat's head to represent the track allowing for leeway. (AC and AC')
5. Measure along the leeway track the distance sailed in 1 hour i.e. 5 miles, AC and AC'.
6. From C and C' lay off the direction and rate of the tidal stream for the same period of time i.e. 330°, 2 miles. Lines CD and C'D'.
7. Join A to D and D' respectively. These lines represent the course and speed made good when on the starboard and port tacks respectively.

     a) starboard tack (AD) = 056° at 4.7 knots.
     b)   port   tack (AD') = 210° at 3.7 knots.

EXAMPLE 26

A yacht finds it necessary to tack to a position 250° distant 12 miles from her departure position. The wind is from the SW and she is able to sail within 45° of the wind. After 2 hours the wind veers to the west and remains constant from this direction.

The direction and rate of the tidal stream is estimated to be 270°, at 1 knot for the first 2 hours, then slack for 2 hours.

The boat's speed on either tack is 5 knots, allowance for leeway 10°.

Find:-   i.   the course and speed made good on the various tacks.

   ii.   the times of altering course if the boat tacks within a three mile limit either side of the original course line.

   iii.   the time of arrival at her destination.

1.   Plot position B 250° distant 12 miles from A. This is the original course line.

2.   Draw lines 3 miles either side of this direction to represent the limit of any tack.

3.   To plot the boat's track starting from A.
      At position A:-
      a) draw in the direction of the wind, SW.
      b) draw a line 45° either side of this direction to represent the boat's head.
      c) draw a line 10° to leeward of the boat's head to represent the track allowing for leeway.
      d) measure along the track the distance sailed in 1 hour, i.e. 5 miles, AC.
      e) from C lay off the direction and rate of the tidal stream, i.e. 270°, 1 mile, CD.
      f) join AD. This line represents the course and speed made good. In the figure, AD represents the course and speed made good on the port tack, AD' the course and speed made good on the starboard tack.
         i.   port   tack 278° at 6 knots.
         ii.   starboard tack 182° at 4.9 knots.

4.   Since there is no change in the wind direction or tidal stream for the next 2 hours plot the track of the boat for that period of time. She will continue on the port tack to position E (1h.5m.) then go about on to the starboard tack following a track parallel to AD' until she has arrived at position F after a total period of 2 hours.

5.   At F it is now necessary to find the new course and speed made good since the wind has veered to the west, the tidal stream now being slack. The plotting is carried out in a similar manner to that at A, the new courses and speeds being:
         i.   port   tack (FG') 325° at 5 knots
         ii.   starboard tack (FG) 215° at 5 knots.

6.   The boat follows the wind round and continues along the track FG until position H is reached (after 2h. 38m.). At H she goes about and follows the track HK parallel to FG'. This track is followed until she is in such a position J (after 3h. 24m.) that by going on to a final tack JB (parallel to FG) she can sail direct to her destination.

The position of J is found by laying off the line BL through B parallel to the track FG. Where this line intersects the track HK at J is the position to alter on to the final tack. She arrives at B after 3h. 39m.

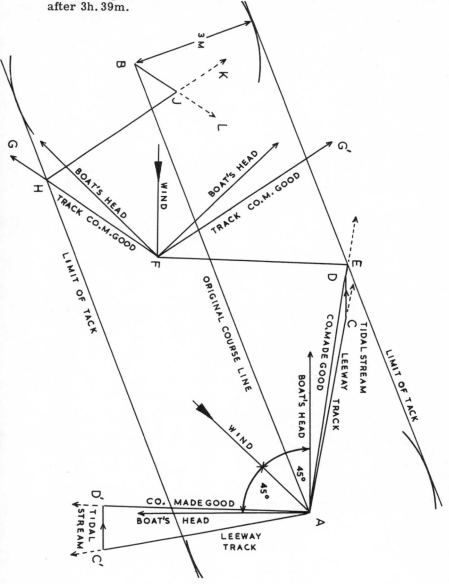

TACKING OR BEATING TO WINDWARD

A sailing vessel which is unable to sail directly to her destination due to the wind direction, should not deviate too far from the original course line. This may be prevented by tacking within a set distance of the course line or by carrying out a "corkscrew" tack.

A "corkscrew" tack consists of tacking within two lines drawn at an angle to the original course line from the destination. By keeping within these two lines the vessel "corkscrews" towards her destination, each tack being shorter than the previous tack.

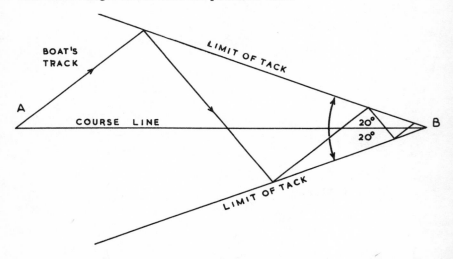

Another form of "corkscrew" tack occasionally employed is to halve the distance between the vessel and her destination each time the original course line is crossed when tacking.

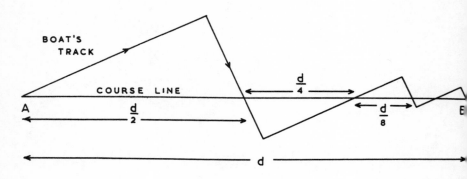

Exercises Nos. 24, 25 and 26 may be worked on any convenient chart.

EXERCISE 24

Position B is 272° distant 25 miles from position A.

1.   Assuming a yacht may tack within 3 miles of this track, wind WSW, and sailing within 50° of the wind, no tide or leeway, find:-
   a) the courses to steer
   b) the distances to sail on each tack from position A to position B.

2.   Assuming a corkscrew tack of 10° either side of the track is followed, find the distances sailed on each tack. The 8th tack is continued until the final tack, i.e. 9th tack, takes the yacht to her destination at B.

EXERCISE 25

Two positions A and B lie on the same parallel of latitude and B is 24 miles due east of A.

Assuming that the boat may not deviate more than 2 miles either side of the line joining A and B, find the courses steered and time on each tack when sailing from A to B. Wind SE, leeway 6°, tide 075° at 1 knot, boat's speed 6 knots. Boat sails within 50° of the wind.

EXERCISE 26

Position B is 252° distant 30 miles from A. The boat's speed is 6 knots, allowance for leeway 5° and she sails within 50° of the wind.

The wind is from the SW for the first 2 hours after which it then veers to the west for an hour and then veers to the NW for the remainder of the time.

The tidal stream for the first 3 hours sets 105° at 1 knot, then slack for 1 hour after which it sets 265° at 1 knot.

Due to shoals, sailing is restricted to 3 miles either side of the course line from A to B.

Assuming that the boat left position A at midnight, find:
   a. the courses steered
   b. the times of altering tack
   c. the time of arrival at her destination.

EXERCISE 27

Chart No. 1431   Variation 7°W., Deviation Card No. 1.

1.   Find the true course and distance from the W. Dyck lightvessel to a position 180° distant 1.3 miles from the Varne lightvessel, thence to a position 180° distant 1 mile from the Royal Sovereign lightvessel and finally to a position with Beachy Head lighthouse bearing 360°, distant 2 miles.

2.   Whilst on passage the following conditions exist.

    i. the wind is SE for 3 hours, then S'ly. for 2 hours, SW for 8 hours, W'ly for 1 hour and then steady from the NW.

    ii. the tide is 040° at 2 knots for 3 hours, slack for 1 hour, 210° at 1.5 knots for 5 hours, slack for 2 hours and then 070° at 2 knots.

In order to make the position off the Royal Sovereign lightvessel and again off Beachy Head a corkscrew tack of 30° either side of the course line is carried out, otherwise the boat is to tack within 3 miles of the original track. She follows the original course line when not tacking.

Boat's speed 7 knots except when closehauled, then it is only 5 knots. Leeway 5° throughout. The yacht is able to sail within 45° of the wind.

Plot the boat's track through the water and find:-

    a) the compass courses steered.
    b) the time on each course and times of changing tack.
    c) E.T.A. at the Royal Sovereign lightvessel and at Beachy Head assuming a departure from the W. Dyck lightvessel at 0000 hours.

THE LOG BOOK

It is essential when sailing to keep a record of the courses sailed, the distance and time on each course, the direction and rate of tidal streams, wind direction and strength, allowances for leeway etc. The position of the boat should be noted on the chart at frequent intervals and when it is not possible to obtain a fix then an estimated position should be shown. The navigator will then know at a glance his position on the chart.

Should no record have been kept, a sudden deterioration in the weather taking place, the navigator being unaware of his position will have great difficulty in setting a course for safety.

The following exercises require the plotting of the various courses sailed and the tidal streams experienced as extracted from log book entries.

Chart No. 1431

EXERCISE 28

A vessel sailing in the Dover Strait had the following entries in the log book.

Time	Course	Error	Wind	L'way	Log	Remarks
0700	223°(C)	8°W	West	5°	0	Off Occ.R.Whis.buoy, Boulogne at 0700 hrs. Co. set 223°(C). Tidal stream 0700 hrs. to 1000 hrs., 200° at 1.5 knots.
1000	290°(C)	15°E	West	5°	30	1000 hrs. a/c 290°(C) log 30. Tidal stream 1000 hrs. to 1200 hrs. 080° at 1 knot. 1200 hrs. to 1500 hrs., 050° at 1.5 knots.
1300	065°(C)	15°W	NW	5°	60	1300 hrs. a/c 065°(C) log 60.
1500	130°(C)	30°W	NW	5°	80	1500 hrs. a/c 130°(C) log 80. Tidal stream 1500 hrs. to 1600 hrs. 140°
1600	130°(C)	30°W	NW	5°	90	at 1 knot.

Find the dead reckoned and estimated positions of the vessel at 1600 hrs.

EXERCISE 29

Chart No. 2159

At 1200 hrs. Corsewall Point Lt. Hse. bore 106°(C)., error 16°W, distant 2 miles. Extracts from the log book were as follows:

Course	Error	Wind	Leeway	Distance Sailed
295°(C)	13°E	SE'ly	nil	10 m.
342°(C)	13°E	SE'ly	5°	7 m.
054°(C)	9°W	S'ly	5°	11 m.
102°(C)	25°W	S'ly	5°	9 m.
175°(C)	25°W	SW'ly	5°	8 m.
228°(C)	7°W	SW'ly	nil	16 m.

Find the boat's position at the end of the final leg.

EXERCISE 30

Chart No. 1411   Variation 8°W., No Deviation.

A vessel cruising in the Irish Sea recorded the following log book entries.

0800 hrs. Skerries Lt. Hse. bearing 118°(C)., distant 2 miles.

Time		Course	Speed Knots	Wind	Leeway
From	To				
0800	1100	290°(C)	7.5	SW	8°
1100	1300	233°(C)	7.0	WSW	5°
1300	1530	198°(C)	7.0	W	10°
1530	1830	118°(C)	7.0	NW	5°

Tidal streams

Time		Dir'n.	Rate Knots
From	To		
0800	1000	020°	1.0
1000	1100	slack	
1100	1200	170°	1.0
1200	1500	190°	1.5
1500	1700	200°	1.0
1700	1830	slack	

At 1830 hrs. the visibility deteriorated and a course was set to a position 270°, distant 1 mile, from Bardsey Is. Lt. Hse.

Find the estimated position at 1830 hrs. and the compass course to steer to reach the position off Bardsey Is. allowing for a tidal stream setting 030° at 1.5 knots. Wind N'ly, leeway 5°, boat's speed 7 knots.

5
Miscellaneous
Exercises

Chart No. 1431   Variation 6°W., Deviation Card No. 2.

1.   Find the true courses and distances between the following positions.

From a position with Beachy Head lighthouse bearing 000° distant 1 mile to a position 180° distant 1 mile from the Royal Sovereign lightvessel, then to a position with the Varne lightvessel abeam to starboard on the approach course, distant 1 mile, then to the north and west of the N.E. Varne buoy, altering course when the buoy is abeam distant ½ mile on the approach course, and finally to the W. Dyck lightvessel.

2.   Find the compass course to steer to make good the first course in question 1, current setting 254° at 1.2 knots, boat's speed 7.5 knots. Find also the speed made good and the time taken to reach the Royal Sovereign lightvessel.

3.   Whilst on the compass course in question 2 the Royal Sovereign lightvessel bore 113°(C) and at the same time Beachy Head lighthouse bore 321°(C). Find the boat's position.

4.   After rounding the Royal Sovereign lightvessel find the compass course to steer to make good the second course in question 1 allowing for a tide setting 218° at 1 knot. Boat's speed 6 knots.

5.   Whilst on the compass course in question 4, Dungeness lighthouse bore 045° (C) and 1 h. 12 m. later the lighthouse bore 304°(C). Give the position of the boat at the time of taking the second bearing as a true bearing and distance from the Varne lightvessel. Tide and boat's speed as in question 4.

6.   With the boat heading 074°(C) the Varne lightvessel bore 2 points on the starboard bow, log 38, and later it bore 1 point abaft the beam, log 42. Set and drift of tide 145° distance ½ mile. Give the position of the boat at the time of taking the second bearing.

7.   Having passed the Varne lightvessel the following horizontal sextant angles were observed:-
Dungeness Lt. Hse. 68°   Folkestone Lt. Hse. 51°   S. Foreland Lt. Hse.
       Find the boat's position.

8.   On the final course in question 1, having rounded the Varne buoy, find the compass course to steer to counteract a tide setting 020° at 1.6 knots, boat's speed 5 knots. Find also the time required to cover the last leg of the passage.

9.   At 1430 hrs., the boat heading 133°(C) at 5 knots, Cap Gris Nez Lt. Hse. bore 181°(C) at the same time as Calais High Lt. (19m) bore 133°(C). At 1630 hrs., Cap Gris Nez Lt. Hse. bore 232°(C) and Calais High Lt. bore 162°(C). Find the direction and rate of the tidal stream experienced between fixes.

10.   From the fix at 1630 hrs. the course was adjusted to reach the W. Dyck lightvessel. Find the compass course to steer to reach the lightvessel allowing for a similar current to that experienced in question 9, speed of boat 5 knots. At what time will she reach the lightvessel?

EXERCISE 32

Chart No. 2159

Variation 10°W throughout, Deviation Card as stated in question.

1.   (a) A vessel in position 54° 48'N., 05° 39'W set course to reach a position with Corsewall Pt. Lt. Hse. bearing 135° distant 1 mile. Find the compass course to steer and speed made good allowing for a tide setting 150° at 2 knots, wind SE., leeway 10°, speed of vessel 6½ knots. Deviation Card No. 1.

(b) After two hours Killantringan Lt. Hse. bore 149°(C) and at the same time Corsewall Pt. Lt. Hse. bore 089°(C). Find the set and drift of the current actually experienced.

(c) Find the compass course to steer and the time to reach the position off Corsewall Pt. from the position in (b) allowing for a similar tide to that actually experienced. Vessel's speed and leeway as in (a).

2.   Heading 348°(C) the Maidens Gp. Fl. light was observed to rise bearing 36° on the port bow. Find the boat's position, range of light as charted. Deviation Card No. 1.

3.   At 0430 hrs. on a course of 123°(C)., speed 7 knots, the Mull of Kintyre light bore 357°(C) and at the same time the Ship light bore 099°(C). At 0450 hrs. the Ship light bore 070°(C) and at 0510 hrs. the same light bore 358°(C). Find the direction and rate of the tidal stream experienced, the course made good and the position of the vessel at 0430 hrs. and 0510 hrs.   Deviation Card No. 2.

4.   Heading 279°(C) from Ayr to Lamlash harbour in poor visibility the radio beacon on Pladda Island bore 36° on the port bow and at the same time Lit. Cumbrae radio beacon bore 51° on the starboard bow. Find the vessel's position. Deviation Card No. 2.

5.   Deviation Card No. 2. Vessel's speed 6 knots.

(a) From a position with Davarr Island Lt. Hse. bearing 180° distant 2 cables the course was set to a position with Pladda Lt. Hse. bearing 000° distant 6 cables, thence to a position midway between the Fl. R. and F. lights at the entrance to the port of Irvine. Find the true courses and distances between these positions.

(b) Find the compass course to steer to make good the first course in (a) allowing for a current setting 359° at 0.6 knots and the speed made good.

(c) Whilst on the course set in (b) Iron Rock Ledges buoy bore 357°(C) and Pladda Island lighthouse bore 120°(C)., 01h. 30m. having elapsed since departing from Davarr Island. Find the boat's position.

(d) After a further 30 minutes Pladda Lt. Hse. was observed abeam to port distant 1 mile. The course was then set to the position off Irvine Bay allowing for a tidal stream setting 000° at 1½ knots. Find the compass course to steer and time to reach Irvine.

(e) After approximately 1h. 30m. on this new course Lady Island lighthouse bore 111°(C) and after a further 40 minutes the lighthouse bore 173°(C)., the tidal stream setting 000° at 1½ knots. Find the boat's position.

6.   Find the vessel's position in each of the following questions:
      (a) Heading 221° (C) Turnberry lighthouse bore 133° (C) and at the
same time a sounding showed 20 fathoms.   Deviation Card No. 2.
      (b) Heading 168° (C) Garroch Head was observed in transit with
Lit. Cumbrae lighthouse and at the same time the peak of Goat Fell bore
231° (C).   Deviation Card No. 2.
      (c) The following horizontal sextant angles were observed from a
yacht off Ailsa Craig:-
Ailsa Craig Lt. Hse. 105° Pladda Lt. Hse. 116° Turnberry Pt. Lt. Hse.
If Ailsa Craig Lt. Hse. bore 224° (C) at the same time, what is the compass deviation?
      (d) Killantringan Lt. Hse. (160 ft.) subtended a vertical sextant
angle of 0° 36' bearing 100^O(C)., boat's head 181^O(C). Deviation Card No. 2.
      (e) Heading 197° (C)., Corsewall Pt. light bore 165° (C) and at the
same time Ailsa Craig light was observed to dip, height of eye 15 ft.
Deviation Card No. 1.
      (f) Heading 217° (C) at 8 knots Ailsa Craig Lt. Hse. bore 242^O(C)
at 1720 hrs. and at 1800 hrs. the Lt. Hse. bore 342° (C).   The tidal
stream was setting 136° at 0.6 knots during this interval.   Required
the position at 1800 hrs.   Deviation Card No. 2.

7.   Heading 045° (C) at 6 knots the Maidens lighthouse bore 280° (C)
distant 2 miles at 1400 hrs.   At 1500 hrs. it was necessary to alter
course 30° to port by compass for fishing craft, the original course
being resumed after a further 30 minutes.   At 1630 hrs. the compass
course was altered by 50° to starboard, the original course again being
resumed at 1710 hrs.   At 1800 hrs. it was decided to set a course to a
position with Pladda Lt. Hse. bearing 325^O(M) distant 2 miles.   Reference to tidal stream tables showed the tidal streams to have been 320°
at $1\frac{1}{2}$ knots from 1400 hrs. to 1600 hrs. and 010° at 1 knot from 1600
hrs. to 1800 hrs.
      Find the compass course to steer to reach the position off Pladda
Lt. Hse. allowing for a current setting 095° at 1 knot and the E.T.A.
Deviation Card No. 2.

EXERCISE 33

Chart No. 1411   Variation 7°W., Deviation Card No. 2.

1.   At 1500 hrs. a vessel heading 270°(C) at 5.5 knots observed Great Ormes Head Lt. Hse. bearing 138°(C) and the centre of Puffin Island bearing 221°(C). From this position the course was laid off to pass 2 miles off Lynas Point Lt. Hse. Find the compass course to steer to make good this new course allowing for a tidal stream setting 130° at 1.6 knots, also the speed made good.

2.   At 1700 hrs. whilst on the course set in question 1, Lynas Pt. Lt. Hse. bore 259°(C) and at 1800 hrs. the lighthouse bore 215°(C). Find the position of the boat at 1800 hrs. and the actual direction and rate of the tidal stream experienced.

3.   From the position at 1800 hrs. the course was then set to a position with the Skerries Lt. Hse. bearing 180° distant 2 miles. The tide is estimated to set 065° at 2 knots, vessel's speed 6 knots. Find the compass course to steer to make good this course and the E.T.A. off the Skerries.

4.   At 1900 hrs. a fix was obtained with Lynas Point bearing 122°(C) and the Middle Mouse bearing 250°(C). Give the position of the vessel as a bearing and distance from the Skerries. Course as in question 3.

5.   At 2045 hrs. Ethel Rock buoy bore 132°(C) at the same time as the Skerries Lt. Hse. was in transit with S. Stack Lt. Hse. Give the position of the fix, course as in question 3.

6.   From the position at 2045 hrs. the vessel maintained her present course until the Skerries Lt. Hse. was abeam to port distant 2.2 miles when the course was altered to a position with the S. Stack Lt. Hse. bearing 090° distant 1½ miles. Find the compass course to steer to counteract a tide setting 295° at 1.5 knots, speed of vessel 6 knots.

7.   At 2200 hrs. the Skerries light was observed bearing 058°(C) and at the same time S. Stack lighthouse bore 193°(C). Find the vessel's position at this time, course as in question 6.

8.   At 2242 hrs. heading 205°(C) at 6 knots S. Stack Lt. Hse. was abeam to port and at the same time the Skerries Lt. Hse. bore 050°(C). From this position the course was laid off to reach a position in 52° 48' N 04° 47' W. Find the compass course to steer to make good this course allowing for a tide estimated to set 180° at 2 knots for the next 4 hours.

9.   At 0050 hrs. Bardsey Is. light was observed to rise bearing 197°(C). From this position the course was adjusted to reach the position in question 8 off Bardsey Is. Give the E.T.A. and compass course to steer to make good this new course, tide setting 180° at 2 knots.

10.   At 0220 hrs. the night being clear, Braich-y-Pwll headland bore 169°(C)., Bardsey Is. light bore 206°(C). Find the vessel's position.

11.   At 0230 hrs. with Braich-y-Pwll abeam to port the course was altered to 176°(C) to pass through Bardsey Sound and when the lighthouse was abeam to starboard distance 2 miles the course was again altered to 119°(C) towards Tremadoc Bay. At 0315 hrs. Bardsey Is. light bore 288°(C)., Pen-y-oil Headland bore 352°(C). Give the position of the vessel at 0315 hrs. and find the compass course to steer to reach a position with St. Tudwals Is. light bearing 000° distant 2 miles. Tidal stream setting 235° at 1 knot, vessel's speed 6 knots.

12.   At 0500 hrs. St. Tudwals Is. light bore 019°(C)., Trwyn Cilan beacon bore 312°(C)., compass course 109°(C). Find the direction and rate of the tidal stream experienced between 0315 hrs. and 0500 hrs. If the tide is now expected to set 240° at 0.5 knots find the compass course to steer and the E.T.A. to reach the fairway buoy off Harlech Point. Vessel's speed 6 knots.

EXERCISE 34

Chart No. 1431

Variation 9°W., throughout.   Deviation Card as stated in the question.

1.   a) At 0450 hrs. a vessel off Cap Gris Nez heading 182°(C) at 5 knots observed the lighthouse to bear 099°(C) and at 0544 hrs. C. d'Alprech lighthouse bore 139°(C). During this time the tide set 209° at 3 knots. Find the vessel's position at 0544 hrs.   Deviation Card No. 1.

b) From the position at 0544 hrs. the course was set to a position midway between the breakwaters at Boulogne.   Find the compass course to steer to reach this position and the E.T.A.   Tidal stream and speed of vessel as in question 1 a.

2.   Heading up Channel on a course of 124°(C) the Royal Sovereign lightvessel was observed to rise at 2300 hrs. and to dip below the horizon at 0045 hrs.   If the vessel's speed was 6 knots, height of eye 15 ft., tidal stream 248° at 2 knots, find:-
a) the position of the vessel at 2300 hrs. and 0045 hrs.
b) the time and distance off when the lightvessel was abeam.
(Running fix).   Deviation Card No. 2.

3.   At 1000 hrs. Dungeness Lt. Hse. bore 4 points on the port bow and 40 minutes later the lighthouse was abeam and at the same time Swallow Bank buoy bore 316°(M).   Give the boat's position at 1040 hrs. as a bearing and distance from the lighthouse and the compass course steered.   Speed of boat 6 knots.

4.   Deviation Card No. 1,   vessel's speed 6 knots.

a) At 2000 hrs., off the French coast, the following horizontal sextant angles were observed:
Cayeux Fl.R.   52° Ault Gp.Occ.   37° Treport Gp.Fl.

From this position the course was set to a position with C. d'Alprech lighthouse abeam distant 1 mile on the approach course.
Find i. the position at 2000 hrs.
ii. the compass course to steer to counteract a tide setting 022° at 1.5 knots, also the speed made good.

b) At 2130 hrs. Pte. du Haut Banc light bore 069°(C) and at 2210 hrs. the light bore 113°(C). Course and speed as in (a). Find the position of the vessel at 2210 hrs., the course and speed made good and the set and drift of the current experienced. (Three bearing problem)

c) From the position at 2210 hrs. the course was adjusted to reach the original position off C. d'Alprech lighthouse allowing for a tide estimated to set 040° at 1.0 knot. Find the compass course to steer and E.T.A. off C. d'Alprech.

5.   Deviation Card No. 2.   Vessel's speed 5 knots throughout.

a) A vessel heading 122°(C) off the Royal Sovereign lightvessel, in foggy weather, obtained a D. F. bearing of the lightvessel as 40° on the port bow and at the same time a sounding showed 20 fathoms. From this position the course was set to a position with Dungeness lighthouse bearing 000°, distant 2 miles. Find the compass course to steer to counteract a current setting 068° at 2 knots.

b) After one hour the D. F. bearing of the Royal Sovereign lightvessel was 10° abaft the port beam and at the same time the Ro. Bn. at Dungeness was heard bearing 4° on the port bow. Find the position of the vessel at this time; course as found in question 5 (a).

c) After a further hour Cap Gris Nez Ro. Bn. bore 19° on the starboard bow and Dungeness Ro. Bn. bore 10° on the port bow and at the same time a sounding showed 21 fathoms. From this position the compass course was then adjusted to reach the position off Dungeness allowing for a tide setting 068° at 1½ knots. Find the compass course to steer and E. T. A. off Dungeness.

6.   Deviation Card No. 2.   Vessel's speed 5 knots.

A vessel off Cap Gris Nez, at 1200 hrs., observed by sextant that the lighthouse subtended a vertical angle of 1° 01' when bearing 118°(C)., course 042°(C). Find the vessel's position at this time.

From the position off Cap Gris Nez the course was set to a position with the W. Dyck lightvessel bearing 090° distant 1½ miles. Find the single compass course to steer to counteract the tide as found from the chart during the next two hours, tidal stream ⊕. High water at Dover 1303 hrs. spring tides.

7.   Find the vessel's position in each of the following questions.

a) Heading 280°(C) the Royal Sovereign lightvessel bore 050°(C) and at the same time Beachy Head lighthouse bore 298°(C). Deviation Card No. 1.

b) The N. E. Varne lightbuoy in transit with the Varne lightvessel bearing 213°(C) and at the same time S. Foreland lighthouse bore 333°(C).

c) The following simultaneous compass bearings were obtained:-
Varne lightvessel bearing 333°(C);
Cap Gris Nez Lt. Hse. bearing 082°(C);
C. d'Alprech Lt. Hse. bearing 143°(C).

Find the position of the vessel and the deviation of the compass.

d) A vessel off C. d'Alprech observed the lighthouse to bear 040°(C) at 2130 hrs., and at 2215 hrs. it bore 120°(C). If the vessel was heading 007°(C) at 8 knots and the tidal stream setting 011° at 2 knots find the position at 2215 hrs. Deviation Card No. 2.

e) Heading 266°(C) the Varne lightvessel (charted height of light 40 ft.) was observed to dip bearing 048°(C). If the height of the observer's eye was 9 ft. and the height of the tide 16 ft. above Chart Datum find the position of the boat. Deviation negligible.

EXERCISE 35

Chart No. 1411　　　Variation 9° W.　　Deviation as per question.

1.　　A vessel steering 005° (C) at 7 knots observed Bailey Head light-house to bear 254° (C) and at the same time the Kish lightvessel bore 199° (C). After 60 minutes Rockabill Lt. Hse. bore 332° (C) and after a further 50 minutes the lighthouse bore 265° (C).

Find the set and drift experienced during this period of 1hr. 50m. and the position of the vessel when Rockabill Lt. Hse. bore 265° (C). Deviation Card No. 1.

2.　　At 1923 hrs. the Codling Lt. V. bore 140° (C)., vessel heading 177° (C) at 6 knots. At 2017 hrs. the lightvessel bore 048° (C).

Find the position of the vessel at 2017 hrs. the tidal information as taken from the chart. High water Liverpool 1758 hrs. Neap Tides. Deviation Card No. 2.

3.　　A vessel heading on a certain course observed the Codling light-vessel bearing 30° on the port bow and after 30 minutes it bore 80° on the port bow. When the lightvessel was abeam to port Wicklow Head lighthouse bore 247°. If the boat's speed was 8 knots, find the true course steered and the position when the lightvessel was abeam.

4.　　A vessel heading 182° (C) at 8 knots observed the Kish lightvessel to rise at 0100 hrs. and 1hr. 30m. later the Codling lightvessel was also observed to rise. If the tidal stream was setting 189° (M) at 2 knots find the position at 0230 hrs. and the time when the Kish Lt. V. was abeam. Deviation Card No. 1.　　Height of eye 15 feet.

5.　　　　Deviation Card No. 1.　Speed of vessel 9 knots.

(a) A vessel heading 269° (C) observed Bardsey Island lighthouse to bear 359° (C)., and at the same time Tudwals Island lighthouse bore 059° (C)., the time being 2100 hrs.

Find the compass course to steer from this position and the E. T. A. to reach a position with the Kish lightvessel bearing 000° distant 1 mile. Tide estimated to set 180° at an average rate of 1.75 knots.

(b) At 0100 hrs. the Codling lightvessel was observed to rise bearing 300° (C). Find the actual set and drift experienced since 2100 hrs. and the course and speed made good.

(c) At 0100 hrs. the course was adjusted to reach the position off the Kish Lt. V. the tidal stream now estimated to set 180° at 1.5 knots. Find the compass course to steer and speed made good. Allow 5° lee-way for a moderate N'ly wind.

(d) At 0200 hrs. the Codling lightvessel bore 265° (C) and at 0300 hrs. the lightvessel bore 193° (C). Assuming the vessel to be steering on the course found in Q. 5(c) at 9 knots, tidal stream 180° at 1.5 knots, leeway 5° for a N'ly wind, find the vessel's position at 0300 hrs.

(e) From the position at 0300 hrs. the course was again adjusted to the position off the Kish Lt. V. Find the compass course to steer and E. T. A. at the Kish Lt. V. tidal effect negligible, leeway now 10° for a fresh NE wind.

6.   A vessel heading 235°(C) at 7.5 knots observed the following compass bearings:- St. Tudwals Lt. Hse. bearing 024°(C)
Trwyn Cilan Bn.   bearing 307°(C)
The course was then set from this position to pass 1½ miles off Bardsey Isle Lt. Hse. tidal effect negligible.   After 1 hour Bardsey Isle lighthouse bore 276° (C) and after a further 1 hour the lighthouse was abeam.

Find the position of the vessel when the lighthouse was abeam, the compass course steered, the course made good and the tidal stream experienced. Deviation Card No. 1.

7.   (a) A vessel heading 315°(C) observed Trwyn Du light to bear 172°(C) and at the same time Great Ormes Head light bore 089°(C). Course was then set to pass 1 mile off Lynas Point.   Find the compass course to steer to counteract a current setting 085° at 1.2 knots. Speed of vessel 6 knots.   Due to a strong offshore wind 8° leeway was allowed. Deviation Card No. 2.

(b) After 1hr. 30m., whilst on the course set in (a), Lynas Point bore 257°(C) and at the same time Moelfre Lt. Hse. bore 192°(C). Find the vessel's position at this time and the actual tidal stream experienced.

8.   (a) A yacht heading 213°(C) observed S. Stack Lt. Hse. on a bearing of 054°(C) and at the same time a sounding showed 21 fathoms. If the height of the tide at this time was calculated as 6 ft. find the boat's position. Deviation Card No. 1.

(b) A vessel off Holyhead Bay observed the horizontal sextant angle between the Skerries Lt. Hse. and S. Stack Lt. Hse. to be 125°. At the same time the vertical angle subtended by S. Stack Lt. Hse. was 00° 28'. Find the boat's position.

(c) Heading 046°(C) off the Skerries a D. F. bearing gave the Ro. Bn. as 24° on the starboard bow and at the same time soundings, corrected, showed 30 fathoms. Give the approximate position of the vessel. Deviation Card No. 2.

(d) Heading 134°(C) the Skerries light was observed to rise bearing 141°(C) height of eye 16 ft. Find the boat's position. Deviation Card No. 2.

(e) Heading 003° (C) Burford Bank N. Can Buoy was in transit with Bailey Head bearing 327° (C) and at the same time the Kish lightvessel bore 061° (C).   Find the vessel's position and the deviation on this heading.

(f) At the same time as No. 3 Kish Bank Buoy was in transit with Great Sugar Loaf Peak the horizontal angle subtended between No. 2 and No. 3 Kish Buoys was 60°. Find the boat's position.

EXERCISE 36

Chart No. 2159   Variation 10°W., Deviation Card No. 1.

1.   A vessel in a position 270° 6 cables from Lit. Cumbrae Lt. Hse., laid off the following courses on the chart:

    a) From the position off Lit. Cumbrae to a position distance 1.5 miles off Holy Is. Alt. Lt. when abeam on the approach course.

    b) From Holy Is. to a position 1 mile off Pladda Is. Lt. Hse. when abeam on the approach course.

    c) From Pladda Is. to a position with the Ship Lt. Hse. bearing 000° distant 1 mile.

Find the true course and distance on each leg of the passage.

2.   At 0930 hrs. the vessel is in the above position off Cumbrae Island. Find the compass course to steer to make good the initial course laid down on the chart. Boat's speed 6 knots, tidal stream 330° at 1 knot, leeway 5° for a SE wind. Find also the speed made good.

3.   At 1100 hrs., on the course found in question 2, Clauchland Pt. bore 217°(C) and at the same time Goat Fell Peak bore 291°(C). Give the position at 1100 hrs. and the actual set and drift experienced since 0930 hrs. Leeway and speed as in question 2.

4.   At 1100 hrs. the course was adjusted to the position off Holy Island allowing for a similar tide to that found in question 3. Speed of vessel is now 5 knots, leeway 5° for a SE wind. Find the compass course to steer and E.T.A. off Holy Is.

5.   At 1230 hrs., compass course as found in question 4, the following fix was obtained. At the same time as Dippin Point was in transit with Pladda Lt. Hse., Holy Is. Alt. Lt. Hse. bore 294°(C). Find the boat's position.

6.   From the position at 1230 hrs. the course was set to the position off Pladda Is. Find the compass course to steer to counteract a current setting 055° at 0.5 knots, speed of boat 5 knots, leeway 6° for a S'ly wind.

7.   At 1345 hrs. Largybeg Point was in transit with Kingscross Point and at the same time Pladda Is. Lt. Hse was abeam to starboard, boat heading 201°(C). Find the position of the boat.

8.   From the position obtained in question 7, the course was then set to the position off the Ship Lt. Hse., tide slack, leeway 10° for a S'ly wind. Find the compass course to steer.

9.   After 1 hr. 15 m. the tide was estimated to set 090° at 2 knots. Find the new compass course to steer to reach the original position off Sanda Is., speed and leeway as in question 8. Give the E.T.A. off the Ship lighthouse assuming the tide to remain constant.

10.   At 1800 hrs. the Ship Lt. Hse. bore 253°(C) and one hour later it bore 292°(C). If the boat is heading 238°(C) at 5 knots, tide setting 088° at 2½ knots, leeway 10° for S'ly wind, find the boat's position at 1900 hrs.

Answers

EXERCISE 1

(a)
50° 54.'8N., 00° 58.'6E.
50° 42.'7N., 00° 27.'0E.
51° 04.'5N., 01° 11.'7E.
50° 41.'9N., 01° 33.'9E.
50° 52.'2N., 01° 35.'2E.
50° 57.'6N., 01° 51.'3E.

(b)
55° 25.'7N., 05° 07.'0W.
55° 15.'1N., 05° 06.'4W.
55° 00.'4N., 05° 09.'4W.
55° 16.'6N., 05° 34.'8W.
55° 25.'9N., 05° 32.'2W.

(c)
52° 57.'9N., 05° 59.'8W.
53° 35.'8N., 06° 00.'4W.
53° 19.'1N., 05° 54.'6W.
53° 24.'8N., 04° 17.'4W.
52° 44.'9N., 04° 47.'9W.

EXERCISE 2

(a) $147\frac{1}{2}°$, 16.4m.
$198\frac{1}{2}°$, 8.0m.
$211\frac{1}{2}°$, 18.0m.
180° , 11.5m.
$279\frac{1}{2}°$, 32.5m.
$036\frac{1}{2}°$, 37.9m.
$045\frac{1}{2}°$, 17.5m.

(b) $145\frac{1}{2}°$, 14.0m.
215° , 20.0m.
$195\frac{1}{2}°$, 15.0m.
322° , 19.7m.
061° , 19.6m.
008° , 17.7m.

(c) 168° , 17.4m.
$154\frac{1}{2}°$, 16.7m.
$122\frac{1}{2}°$, 35.6m.
005° , 33.2m.
321° , 28.3m.
261° , 25.8m.

EXERCISE 3

(a) 50°51.'8N., 01°33.'7E. (b) 55°39.'2N., 05°27.'1W. (c) 53°21.'8N., 03°53.'2W.

EXERCISE 4

(a) (i) 045°(C)., 157°(C)., 213°(C)., $317\frac{1}{2}°$(C)., 090°(C)., 191°(C).,
301°(C).

(ii) 059°(C)., 166°(C)., $275\frac{1}{2}°$(C)., 358°(C).

(iii) $015\frac{1}{2}°$, $108\frac{1}{2}°$, $208\frac{1}{2}°$, 264°, $308\frac{1}{2}°$, 343°.

(b) (i) 059°, 097°, $158\frac{1}{2}°$, $027\frac{1}{2}°$, 206°, 318°, $105\frac{1}{2}°$, $346\frac{1}{2}°$.

(ii) $081\frac{1}{2}°$(C)., 144°(C)., $178\frac{1}{2}°$(C)., 239°(C)., $272\frac{1}{2}°$(C)., 297°(C).

EXERCISE 5

Chart 1431:- 263°(C)., 18.9m; $232\frac{1}{2}°$(C)., 6.6m; 246°(C)., 34.0m.
Chart 1411:- $062\frac{1}{2}°$(C)., 10.4m; 359° (C)., 15.3m; 289°(C)., 7.4m.
Chart 2159:- $200\frac{1}{2}°$(C)., 17.8m; 219° (C)., 21.3m; 068°, 2.3m.

EXERCISE 6

(a) 50° 28.'3N., 01° 29.'0E.
(c) 50° 58.'2N., 01° 09.'5E.
(e) 50° 52.'8N., 01° 21.'6E. or 50° 52.'4N., 01° 29.'8E.
(f) 50° 53.'7N., 01° 32.'6E.

(b) 51° 03.'3N., 01° 26.'2E.
(d) 50° 52.'3N., 01° 00.'4E.

Page 58   EXERCISES IN COASTAL NAVIGATION

EXERCISE 7

(a) 55° 18.'8N., 04° 53.'1W. (b) 55° 43.'3N., 05° 07.'1W., dev. $3\frac{1}{2}$° E.
(c) 55° 31.'3N., 05° 01.'7W. (d) 55° 35.'2N., 04° 56.'8W., dev. $13\frac{1}{2}$° E.
(e) 55° 09.'6N., 05° 16.'7W. (f) 55° 32.'8N., 04° 52.'2W.
(g) 55° 15.'9N., 05° 12.'7W. (h) 55° 22.'0N., 05° 09.'2W.

EXERCISE 8

(a) 53° 29.'0N., 04° 23.'8W.   (b) 52° 51.'1N., 05° 52.'4W.
(c) 52° 51.'1N., 05° 35.'6W.   (d) 53° 30.'7N., 04° 13.'1W.
(e) 53° 27.'4N., 04° 36.'7W.   (f) 53° 19.'4N., 04° 46.'9W.

EXERCISE 9

1) 272°, 7.3 knots   2) $279\frac{1}{2}$°   3) 067°, 7.8 knots   4) 032°, 6.5 knots.

EXERCISE 10

1) 323°, 4.65 knots   2) $159\frac{1}{2}$° (C)., 4.1 knots   3) 048°, 6.3 knots
4) 198° (C).

EXERCISE 11

1) 223° (C)., 22.4m., E.T.A. 1316 hrs.   2) 188°, 1.1 knots.
3) 232° (C)., E.T.A. 1251 hrs.

EXERCISE 12

026°, 1.2m.

EXERCISE 13

041°, 1.3 knots.   (Co. 281°, error 1° E)

EXERCISE 14

1) 50° 42.'6N., 01° 28.'5E.   2) 50° 55.'0N., 01° 34.'2E.

EXERCISE 15

1) 55° 17.'1N., 05° 00.'5W.   2) 55° 21.'9N., 05° 14.'0W.

EXERCISE 16

1) 53° 06.'6N., 05° 35.'5W.   2) 52° 43.'5N., 04° 56.'6W.

EXERCISE 17

1) Set 149°, drift 2m., 50° 23.'8N., 01° 25.'4E.
2) $019\frac{1}{2}$° (C).   3) 1.6 m.

EXERCISE 18

1) $197\frac{1}{2}$°   2)(i) 002°   (ii) 1.6 knots   (iii) 55° 04.'4N., 05° 16.'2W.

EXERCISE 19

1) 53° 27.'5N.,   04° 08.'5W.
   53° 28.'2N.,   04° 25.'0W.
   287° at 1.5 knots.
   3.5 miles at 1249 hrs.

2) 53° 32.'3N.,   05° 51.'6W.
   159° at 1.5 knots.
   205° (C)., E.T.A. 0305 hrs.

EXERCISE 20

1) ◈ H 211° at 0.5K.
3) ◈ K 351° at 0.3K.
5) ◈ G 206° at 3.5K.
7) ◈ A 328° at 0.6K.
9) ◈ F 246° at 0.4K.
11) ◈ I 222° at 0.4K.

2) ◈ E 027° at 2.9K.
4) ◈ M 228° at 1.0K.
6) ◈ D 002° at 0.6K.
8) ◈ H 002° at 1.5K.
10) ◈ J 088° at 2.2K.
12) ◈ C tides weak and irregular

EXERCISE 21

1)   085°, 40.8m.
2) ◈ Q   068°, 1.2K. av; $116\frac{1}{2}°$ (C).
   ◈ M   044°, 1.0K. av; $120\frac{1}{2}°$ (C).
   ◈ K   012°, 0.8K. av; 121° (C).
3)   E.T.A. 1537 hrs.
4)   50° 49.'N., 01° 30.'E.

EXERCISE 22

1)   187°, 28.3m.
2) (a) 190° (C)., (b) 189° (C).,
   (c) $190\frac{1}{2}°$ (C)., (d) $191\frac{1}{2}°$ (C).
       E.T.A. 1606 hrs.
3) $246\frac{1}{2}°$ (C)., speed 3.0 knots.

EXERCISE 23

1)   162°, 17m; 199°, 23.6m.
2)   Tidal streams:- 002° at 1.7K., 029° at 1.7K., 177° at 0.3K.,
                      205° at 1.5K., 204° at 2.3K.
      Courses:- $170\frac{1}{2}°$ (C)., 174° (C)., $166\frac{1}{2}°$ (C)., 196° (C).,
                $195\frac{1}{2}°$ (C)., $195\frac{1}{2}°$ (C).
      E.T.A. Codling Lt.V. 1058 hrs; No.5 buoy 1326 hrs.

EXERCISE 24

1) (a) $297\frac{1}{2}°$; $197\frac{1}{2}°$. (b) 7m; 6.2m; 14m; 4.7m; 3.6m.
2) 7.4m; 6.4m; 10m; 2.7m; 4.1m; 1.1m; 1.7m; 0.8m; 1.3m.

EXERCISE 25

Course	Time on each tack	Dist. on each tack
085°;	1h.27m;	10.2m.
185°;	43m;	4.0m.
085°;	2h.00m;	14.4m.
185°;	10m;	0.9m.

EXERCISE 26

Steers 275° until 0120 hrs., then 175° until 0200 hrs., when the wind veers to the west. Course is then 220° until 0224 hrs., then 320° until 0300 hrs., when the wind veers to the NW. The course is now set direct to the destination, heading $257\frac{1}{2}°$ until 0400 hrs., then $253\frac{1}{2}°$.
E.T.A. 0613 hrs.

EXERCISE 27

1)   252°. 24.0m; 247°, 34.1m; $272\frac{1}{2}°$, 7.8m.

2)
0000 hrs. to 0300 hrs.	$238\frac{1}{2}°$,	$231\frac{1}{2}°$(C).
0300 hrs. to 0400 hrs.	247°,	240° (C).
0400 hrs. to 0500 hrs.	$250\frac{1}{2}°$.	244° (C).
0500 hrs. to 0708 hrs.	270°,	$266\frac{1}{2}°$(C).
0708 hrs. to 0811 hrs.	180°,	181° (C).
0811 hrs. to 0900 hrs.	270°,	$266\frac{1}{2}°$(C).
0900 hrs. to 1017 hrs.	270°,	$266\frac{1}{2}°$(C).
1017 hrs. to 1042 hrs.	180°,	181° (C).
1042 hrs. to 1100 hrs.	270°,	$266\frac{1}{2}°$(C).
1100 hrs. to 1236 hrs.	270°,	$266\frac{1}{2}°$(C).
1236 hrs. to 1300 hrs.	180°,	181° (C).
1300 hrs. to 1331 hrs.	225°,	$218\frac{1}{2}°$(C).
1331 hrs. to 1400 hrs.	315°,	$322\frac{1}{3}°$(C).
1400 hrs. to 1430 hrs.	$265\frac{1}{2}°$,	261° (C).

3)   E.T.A.   Royal Sovereign lightvessel   1100 hrs.
                Beachy Head lighthouse   1430 hrs.

EXERCISE 28

D.R. pos'n: 50° 47′.6N., 01° 12′.4E.
Est. pos'n: 50° 45′.8N., 01° 19′.4E.

EXERCISE 29

55° 06′N., 05° 11′.7W.

EXERCISE 30

52° 51′.2N., 04° 59′.1W.   Course 150°(C).

EXERCISE 31

1) 100°, 7.9m; 063°, 34.6m;
   044°, 5.5m; $086\frac{1}{2}°$, 19.3m.
2) 125°(C)., 6.4 knots, 1h. 14m.
3) 50° 42′.3N., 00° 21′.6E.
4) $074\frac{1}{2}°$(C).
5) $252\frac{1}{2}°$, 8.5m.
6) 50° 57′.3N., 01° 16′.2E.
7) 50° 58′.9N., 01° 19′.2E.
8) 133°(C)., 3h. 34m.
9) 354°, 2.0 knots.
10) 146°(C)., 1805 hrs.

EXERCISE 32
1) (a) 068°(C)., 5.8K.   (b) 127°, 3.4m.   (c) 078°(C)., 1h.06m.
2) 54°48'.6N., 05°20'.4W.
3) 090° at 2.1 knots, 090°, 55°14'.5N.,05°42'.9W.
   55°14'.5N.,05°32'.3W.
4) 55°29'.9N., 04°47'.5W.
5) (a) 094°, 14.5m; 052°, 18m.   (b) 134°(C)., 5.9 knots.
   (c) 55°25'.3N.,05°16'.3W.   (d) 085°(C)., 2h.45m.
   (e) 55°35'.3N.,04°47'.5W.
6) (a) 55°20'.0N.,04°51'.8W.   (b) 55°43'.4N.,05°07'.2W.
   (c) 55°19'.0N.,05°00'.0W. 9½°E.(d) 54°51'.2N.,05°13'.0W.
   (e) 55°02'.3N.,05°10'.3W.   (f) 55°12'.7N.,05°04'.1W.
7) 059½°(C)., 1926 hrs.

EXERCISE 33
1) 282½°(C)., 4 knots.
2) 53°25'.7N.,04°15'.7W.   142° at 1.5 knots.
3) 263°(C)., 2057 hrs.
4) 079½°, 8.8m.
5) 53°27'.4N., 04°34'.8W.
6) 205½°(C)., 5.8 knots.
7) 53°22'.0N., 04°42'.0W.
8) 199°(C).
9) 197½°(C)., 0235 hrs.
10) 52°48'.5N., 04°46'.7W.
11) 52°45'.6N., 04°42'.1W.   110°(C).
12) 244° at 1.1 knots, 075°(C)., 0716 hrs.

EXERCISE 34
1) (a) 50°45'.8N., 1°28'.1E.   (b) 094°(C)., 0655 hrs.
2) (a) 50°33'.5N., 00°17'.9E.,   50°31'.9N., 00°28'.8E.
   (b) 10.5m., 0023 hrs.
3) 083°, 4m., 002°(C).
4) (a) i) 50°10'.3N., 01°20'.1E.   ii) 030°(C)., 7.5 knots.
   (b) 50°24'.3N., 01°28'.4E.   021° at 6.8 knots, 065° at 1.3 knots.
   (c) 019½°(C)., 0048 hrs.
5) (a) 076°(C).   (b) 50°41'.1N.,00°29'.3E.   (c) 064°(C)., 2h.24m.
6) 087½°(C)., 50°53'N., 01°31'.8E.

7) (a) 50°41'.0N., 00°23'.8E.
   (b) 51°02'.7N., 01°25'.5E.
   (c) 50°50'.6N., 01°22'.2E.   dev. 5½°E.
   (d) 50°44'.3N., 01°28'.5E.
   (e) 50°48'.0N., 01°06'.0E.

EXERCISE 35

1) 107°, 1.7m; 53°37'N., 05°54.'4W.
2) 52°58.'5N., 05°44.'2W.
3) 152°, 53°01.'8N., 05°44.'8W. or 341°, 53°04.'0N., 05°36.'5W.
4) 53°13.'7N., 05°45.'1W. 01h.56m.
5) (a) 332°(C)., 04h.04m.   (b) 174°, 9.6m; $310\frac{1}{2}°$, 7.1 knots.
   (c) 339°(C)., 7.8 knots. (d) 53°10.'4N., 05°40.'6W.
   (e) 334°(C)., 04h.18m.
6) 52°42.'1N., 04°46.'8W. $253\frac{1}{2}°$(C)., 095° at 2.25 knots.
7) (a) 274°(C).   (b) 53°25.'2N., 04°11.'8W. 077° at 1.7 knots.
8) (a) 53°17.'1N., 04°44.'5W.   (b) 53°22.'3N., 04°42.'5W.
   (c) 53°22.'3N., 04°45.'2W. or 53°21.'0N., 04°49.'0W.
   (d) 53°30.'6N., 05°03.'8W.   (e) 53°17.'7N., 05°58.'5W. 6°E.
   (f) 53°11.'7N., 05°49.'5W.

EXERCISE 36

1) $185\frac{1}{2}°$, 12.3m; 203°, 6.2m;
   240°, 19.4m.
2) $178\frac{1}{2}°$(C)., 5.1 knots.
3) 55°36'N., 05°01.'7W. 317°, 2.3m.
4) 167°(C)., 1221 hrs.
5) 55°30.'6N., 05°00.'9W.
6) 201°(C).
7) 55°25.'1N., 05°04.'6W.
8) 227°(C).
9) 238°(C). E.T.A. 1912 hrs.
10) 55°15.'9N., 05°32.'4W.

Index

Dev. Card No. 1　　　　　　　　Dev. Card No. 2

Compass Heading	Deviation	Magnetic Heading	Compass Heading	Deviation	Magnetic Heading
000°	4° W	356°	000°	16° E	016°
011¼°	6° W	005¼°	011¼°	13° E	024¼°
022½°	8° W	014½°	022½°	9° E	031½°
033¾°	10° W	023¾°	033¾°	4° E	037¾°
045°	12° W	033°	045°	0°	045°
056¼°	14° W	042¼°	056¼°	4° W	052¼°
067½°	15° W	052½°	067½°	7° W	060½°
078¾°	16° W	062¾°	078¾°	11° W	067¾°
090°	15° W	075°	090°	14° W	076°
101¼°	13° W	088¼°	101¼°	18° W	083¼°
112½°	11° W	101½°	112½°	21° W	091½°
123¾°	8° W	115¾°	123¾°	23° W	100¾°
135°	5° W	130°	135°	24° W	111°
146¼°	3° W	143¼°	146¼°	23° W	123¼°
157½°	0°	157½°	157½°	21° W	136½°
168¾°	3° E	171¾°	168¾°	18° W	150¾°
180°	6° E	186°	180°	14° W	166°
191¼°	9° E	200¼°	191¼°	10° W	181¼°
202½°	12° E	214½°	202½°	7° W	195½°
213¾°	13° E	226¾°	213¾°	3° W	210¾°
225°	14° E	239°	225°	0°	225°
236¼°	14° E	250¼°	236¼°	3° E	239¼°
247½°	13° E	260½°	247½°	7° E	254½°
258¾°	12° E	270¾°	258¾°	10° E	268¾°
270°	10° E	280°	270°	13° E	283°
281¼°	9° E	290¼°	281¼°	17° E	298¼°
292½°	7° E	299½°	292½°	20° E	312½°
303¾°	3° E	306¾°	303¾°	22° E	325¾°
315°	1° E	316°	315°	23° E	338°
326¼°	1° W	325¼°	326¼°	22° E	348¼°
337½°	3° W	334½°	337½°	21° E	358½°
348¾°	4° W	344¾°	348¾°	19° E	007¾°
000°	4° W	356°	000°	16° E	016°

Printed and bound in Great Britain by
Robert Hartnoll (1985) Ltd., Bodmin, Cornwall